OVER MY DEAD BODY

OVER
MY DEAD BODY

June Opie

NEW YORK
E. P. DUTTON & CO., INC.
1957

FOR
MY MOTHER
AND
MARJORIE BENNETT, S.R.N.

CONTENTS

OVER MY DEAD BODY

Chapter 1

THE END OF A JOURNEY

━━━━━◦◦◦◦◦◦◦◦◦◦◦◦◦━━━━━

"Can't see a thing," said Peter.

"Neither can I."

We looked beyond the silvery lines curling away from the sides of the ship and tried to penetrate further into the echoing purple of the night. Where was this island? According to the flag that the Captain had pinned to the chart, it should be, at any moment, about a quarter of a mile to starboard.

"You sure it was the Indian Ocean?" I queried.

"Now look here, Swan—you saw that flag in position on the map as we came from dinner tonight, and you know quite well that it was stuck in the Indian Ocean." Peter spoke with a hint of impatience.

"By the Old Man's reckoning, we should see it any time now."

"You've been saying that for the last twenty minutes."

"Well—if you don't want to stay up any longer, why don't you go to bed?"

I shrugged my shoulders and focused my eyes on my immediate surroundings. It seemed that all the passengers had stayed up to "spot" the island.

"I wonder why a ship doesn't capsize when all its weight of passengers is on one side?" I asked idly.

Peter was silent.

"I think I'll go to bed."

"All right."

"Good night, Peter."

"Good night, Swan."

I walked down the deck and was stepping into the smokers'

1

lounge when I heard a chain of broken crackles which meant that someone was going to make an announcement over the loud-speaker. It was the Captain: "I feel I must remind the passengers that this is the morning of April the First . . . commonly known as April Fool's Day. Sleep Well."

"So——" Peter's eyes were alight with laughter. "One up for the old man. What a brain wave! Sorry I kept you up though."

"I wouldn't have missed this for worlds."

"Missed what? The last few seconds?"

"Yes." I was still laughing.

"Only the last few?"

"Yes—oh, you mean, while we were watching and waiting?"

"Yes."

"I enjoyed that, while you were with me."

"But I was with you all the time."

"No you weren't. Round about half past one you got quite impersonal—left me, and sort of became merged in the night."

"Oh, for heaven's sake, Swan—what rot!" He was looking at me with a wide grin and shaking his head. "Do you want to lie in, in the morning, or will you be up for our walk as usual?"

"I'll be up."

Peggy Foster, a fellow New Zealander who shared my cabin, was sitting on her bunk putting curlers in her coarse red hair.

"One thing about ship-life, there's always plenty of time to make up for lost sleep." She swung her legs into bed. "You won't be walking before breakfast?"

"Oh yes—at least, I've told Peter I would. Coming?"

Peggy pulled the sheet round her bare shoulders and groaned. "No, I'm not. I can't keep pace with you two long-legged things."

As I undressed, washed myself, and cleaned my teeth, I wondered if my enthusiasm was tiresomely unbounded. But it was my first long sea voyage, I was twenty-one, had never known a day's illness, and all this was such an adventure that I did not have to seek enjoyment. It was there, in everything. It was in the harmony of the sea and sky, in the creak and sway of the ship: in the conglomeration of humanity that lived on

2

board and the fish that lived in the sea. Every port meant the fascination and excitement of the unexplored. Life was more than sweet; it was overflowing with richness.

A week later, Peter and I were striding round the deck, which at that hour was free of deck-chairs, gossip, and inert bodies.

"There is a possibility," Peter said, "that we'll have a number of days ashore at Port Said."

"Cheers. There'll be plenty of time to see Cairo?"

"Yes, but there are some pretty bad riots in Cairo at the moment."

"Can't we go through, then?"

"Yes, but only under police protection. Cooks Tours—or me."

"If you can get police protection, why can't I?"

"Provided with a certificate of security from the police, I should be considered safe, because I know Cairo—also, I am a man." This was a blow because I always went off on my own when we hit port. I found that I could see more of the things I wanted to see if I was alone.

Peter ground a cellophane bag, half-full of coloured popcorn, into the sand with his heel, his expression one of extreme distaste. We were at the Pyramids of Gizeh. It was hot which was expected; there were flies, which were accepted; there were hundreds of loud mouths belonging to milling hordes, which were neither expected nor acceptable. There were lolly papers everywhere, the din was incredible, and the scene one of brassy cheapness: a twentieth-century violation of the resting place of the ancient Egyptian kings.

"Oh, Peter, I'm so disappointed."

"We'll tackle them again, tonight. Things ought to have cooled down a bit by then."

We went back to Cairo, to an exhibition of Egyptian painting which was excellent. We returned to Gizeh at half-past nine. A night breeze swept the sand, levelling the holes champed by hundreds of feet. Nothing remained except a native with his camel, a blessed peace, and the pyramids

3

up-thrust against an indigo sky. We stood at the base of the greatest.

"Can we go up, Peter? I mean, are we allowed?"

"Yes, of course. I know the way. I'll have a word with that chap over there, and make sure it's all in order."

He was back in a few seconds indicating the first step of the ascent. He climbed onto it, then turned to look down. "Whatever are you doing, Swan?"

"Taking my stockings off. I don't want to get them scragged."

"I'd leave them on, if I were you. This is the worst place in the world for bugs, and stockings do afford some protection."

I left them on, and began climbing. It was not as difficult as I had anticipated but I was puffing by the time we reached the summit, which, to my surprise, was a platform about thirty feet square. Standing on stones quarried on the banks of the Nile we could see the river itself, a strip of silver trailing through Cairo, then passing into the Egyptian night. Left to myself, I was at last coming to grips with the place. Peter at last ventured a remark. "Are you camping here for the night?"

"No, I'm sorry."

"Happy?"

"Yes, thanks to you. I should never have come back, you know. I had no idea Egypt could be so beautiful."

"Pity it's such a devil of a place for disease."

"Good heavens, Peter! You've got bugs in your bonnet. Let's go down."

Peggy, who shared my cabin, was loud in her lamentations when she heard we had really found Egypt at the top of the Cheops Pyramid, but she was not when she saw my stockings.

"Why didn't you take them off, you ass?"

"Peter advised me not to. He's frightened of bugs."

"Bugs!" Peggy's voice rose in astonishment. "The man must be mad! No bug would stand a chance with you. I've never met anyone who looks more alive, or who seems to enjoy life, as much as you do. Were you nourished on a patent vitalizer, or something?"

My mouth was full of toothpaste and half the tooth-brush.

4

THE END OF A JOURNEY

"Nope. Lovely home life though. Little house on the beach, at the mouth of a river that spills into the sea. Sunshine, sand, climbing hills in my young days, mountains as I grew older—swimming always. Had to go away for my education, but made for home when possible. Be a pal and bring me my pyjamas, please."

Peggy hung my pyjamas over the towel rack. "Go on with your story," she said.

"That's all there is."

"What about family?"

"Mother and father—grand people. If they've ever had a row, I've certainly never heard them. Very fond and very proud of them—they're fairly old though. A brother and sister older than me. My brother was killed in the war." I climbed into the bath.

"Sister like you?"

"Not a scrap. She's got dark hair and quite a different shape. She's also got a wonderful nature, but is very shy."

Peggy laughed. "You certainly can't be alike."

We had a lot of fun seeing as much as we could of Cairo before returning to Port Said.

At sea again, we read our mail and talked. Peter's bug theory was proving correct, because numbers of the passengers were down with attacks of diarrhoea and vomiting. Peggy and I had taken into our cabin a small three-year-old whose mother was one of the victims. A pale, elfin child, with a serious expression that hid an inner vitality, Jenny was a delight, and the boys spent most of her waking hours performing clownish acts in an endeavour to make her laugh. Stephen was the most successful as a clown, and Peter as a storyteller, which left Allen to show his skill as a nurse. The finals of all deck games were in progress, which meant that we were sometimes required to play, so little Jenny had a constant change of chaperone. She did not seem to mind, and when we were all together she sat contentedly on someone's knee while we talked.

In the midst of the babble, when we were twenty-four hours out from Port Said, Peter jumped to his feet, holding his hand aloft in a bid for silence.

5

"Ladies and gentlemen, it gives me great pleasure to invite you to a party this evening, to be held in my cabin. I shall accept no refusals."

"What on earth are you throwing a party for?" asked Stephen, a theological student with an imp of devilry that should make his parishioners' hair stand on end in years to come.

"Actually, old chap, it's my birthday."

"Oh, Peter," I cried, "why didn't you tell us when we were ashore?"

"To prevent any opportunity of carrying out what is obviously in your mind at the moment . . . viz., the purchase of gifts. Eight-thirty suit everyone?"

In the room were fourteen young people, a piano, and a table that was loaded with food. I slipped an envelope under a plate of potato crisps. "What's that, June?" someone asked.

"Something for Peter."

A pair of angry blue eyes were turned on me. "Whatever did you do that for, Swan, when I asked especially——"

"It's only a stupid card I drew myself. Thought it might amuse you, but if there's going to be a fuss about it, I can take it back."

There was a hand on my shoulder. "Sorry, I thought for a moment you had gone and bought me something from the ship's store. Should have known you wouldn't." He opened the envelope, unfolded the card, and burst into a gale of laughter. But he would not allow anyone to see it.

"What's he keeping it so close for, June?"

"I don't know. It's quite innocuous, really. Perhaps he'll put it under his pillow at night and dream sweet dreams of me."

"Dream of you?" Peter raised his eyebrows. "Any dream of you would be one hell of a nightmare!"

The room rang with laughter. Sallies and laughter were predominant throughout the evening, but we could, and did, maintain an appreciative silence when anyone was performing. An Australian with glorious green eyes played the flute, Peter the piano, and Stephen possessed a really fine bass voice. It was a grand party because everyone was so much a part of it: for a fleeting moment I wondered what my twenty-seventh birthday would be like. At half-past ten I caught Peggy's eye and nodded towards the door. A few seconds later she joined me out on the deck.

"What's up?"

"I've got a deuce of a pain, in my back. I'm afraid I can't stand it any longer—I'm off to bed, with a hotty."

"A hotty—on a night like this! You poor old thing, you must feel grim. I'll come along with you."

"No, I'd rather you didn't, if you don't mind. I'm better alone. What I want you to do is to make my excuses to Peter, please. Tell him I'm terribly sorry. Better tell him the truth, but keep it to yourselves."

"Will you let me get the doctor?"

"No, please, Peggy. The poor man is flat out with this diarrhoea and vomiting business. Just do what I ask. I'll be all right in the morning."

I walked back to the cabin, filled a hot-water bottle from the bathroom, undressed in the dark for fear of waking Jenny, then climbed into bed, only to find that I could get no rest. It seemed hours before Peggy appeared.

"Slept at all?" she whispered, her face close to mine.

"No. Have you got any aspirins handy? I'd wake the infant finding mine."

Noise of a drawer opening slowly, a shuffle, rattles against a glass bottle, and two tablets were pushed into my hand. "Do you want any water?"

"No, I can swallow them without. Thanks a lot."

Trickles were running all over me, down my arms, down my legs, round my neck, down my back, and everything was wet; pyjamas, hair, bedclothes. Carefully arching my back, I prepared myself for pain. It had gone, but fearing a recurrence, I moved cautiously. A knock came on the door.

"How are you?" said Peggy.

"Fine, thanks."

"The pain?"

7

"Gone."

"I'm so glad. Everyone is quite upset. Peter was at the cabin door this morning before I had dressed Jenny, and we've all been taking it in turns looking in on you at intervals."

"All of you? But I thought I asked you not to tell the others."

"My dear girl, I had to, to explain your absence at breakfast and lunch."

"Breakfast and lunch!" I was incredulous. "What is the time now?"

"Just after two."

"Peggy—just what did you give me last night? No fooling."

"A couple of kill-me-quicks. My father is a doctor, I am a nurse, and I am not in the habit of dishing out dope indiscriminately. And you certainly needed something more than aspirins last night."

"Well, I'm better anyway, thanks to you. Let's forget all about my back."

Jenny ran along the deck to greet me. "You'se been naughty —you'se been sleepin' in." Catching her up in my arms I walked towards a familiar group engaged in a game of deck golf.

Stephen looked speculatively at the calm Mediterranean. "Awful thing, seasickness. We're glad to see you again."

I trod hard on his foot.

Peter glanced up. "It's obvious you are fully recovered."

"Peter, be a dear, and open a tin of your peaches, please. I'm famished." I ate the whole tinful before going down to afternoon tea.

The voyage had been unusually calm, as nothing more than a light breeze ever seemed to disturb the sea, but we entered the Bay of Biscay to encounter a storm that made light of us in its fury. A mad sea, with the shuddering hulk of our ship in it, wrought havoc among the passengers. If things did not fall on bodies, bodies fell over things. A steward was thrown to the floor of the dining-room, breaking a rib, and as he lay there a plate whizzing through space crashed on his chin and left a horrible gash. But the number of victims from breakages was as nothing compared with those in the throes of seasickness.

With Jenny clinging to my hand I was unable to walk steadily against the reel of the ship and the fierceness of the gale that swept the deck, so I wedged myself into a corner, holding her against me, in order to let her see something of the storm before going to bed. A white-clad figure stopped in front of us. "Jenny bearing up?"

"Yes, Sister, thank goodness." Over the top of the small head pushed against my legs I mouthed the word "mother".

"She's properly down to it, poor thing."

"Is there anything I can do below to help?"

Sister hesitated for a moment, then said, "Well, would you mind helping with the children who are well? The ones whose mothers are ill? They've got to be put to bed, and there isn't a stewardess who has a moment to spare."

"Of course, I'll put Jenny down first."

It was nine o'clock when I came on deck for a breath of fresh air.

As I walked over to the rail, Stephen passed me without speaking. The next moment a voice at my side said, "Why so forlorn, my Swan?"

I shrugged. "I am deserted. And Stephen just went by without a word——"

"Probably afraid to open his mouth. This is glorious, isn't it?" He swept his arm seawards.

"Yes . . . you know, Peter, it makes me so excited I should like to shout at it. Crazy, aren't I?"

"No. Just alive—really alive, that's all."

The storm ceased at midnight. It was followed by days of sunshine, although the temperature dropped considerably as we sailed up the English Channel, searching the coastline for landmarks made familiar to us by our families, our friends, or our reading. England was home. I began to think it something of a misnomer when we berthed at Tilbury, because we did not appear to be at all welcome. A dock strike was on. We were scheduled to disembark immediately after an early breakfast, but with no one except the ship's crew to handle all the luggage, it was three o'clock before the first passengers walked down the gangway.

With an uncommon surname initial I was first through the customs and into the boat train. After spreading gear about to reserve seats for the others, I settled back mentally complimenting the English on the kindliness and efficiency of their porters. There was a rap on the door of the carriage. It was my porter.

"Excuse me, miss," as he lifted his cap, "but it's usual to tip."

I was acutely embarrassed, for my father had schooled me on this tipping business, so I apologized and handed him some money, with the injunction to buy his wife a pot of New Zealand ferns.

We had a long wait on that train, but eventually everyone was through and we were on our way to St Pancras, sliding past backyard upon backyard; identical except for the clothes pegged on the lines. At the station we had a frantic struggle to gather our luggage together again before taking farewell of one another. Stephen was off to Cambridge during the following week; Peter, who was going to Italy to study frescoes, was leaving England in two days; I intended establishing myself in a temporary billet, for a fortnight or so, while I looked about for permanent digs.

I checked my luggage a third time before turning to look for Peter. He was standing close beside me searching his pockets.

"I'm looking for my pen and a piece of paper."

"What for?"

"To take your address."

"But I don't know my address . . . you see, I don't know where I'm going, yet."

"You don't, WHAT?" Peter's searching came to an abrupt halt as he looked at me in open-mouthed astonishment.

"Don't worry, I'll find somewhere to sleep."

"But, Swan—you must be out of your mind! You're on your own, and you can't just hurl yourself into London and not have some definite place to go. It's an enormous place—you've no idea." Peter's long hands were describing London's immensity and my idiocy in the air.

I caught one of them in mine. "Peter—I had all this out with my father, before I left New Zealand. I haven't much time before I start my speech therapy studies, and I want to make the most of it. There's only one way of accomplishing that, and that is to be free—independent—on one's own. The people in London are not barbarians; they speak the same language as I do, and my position is exactly the same as that of a stranger arriving in Auckland seeking accommodation. I'm fit and strong and intend asking a taxi-driver or a policeman to direct me to a decent hostel for women." I drew a deep breath and said more slowly: "Now you may speak."

Peter grinned. "You win, Miss Independence, but how can I get in touch with you?"

I did not quite know what to say. Peter had been an ideal ship-board companion but there was an air of restlessness or eagerness about him that gave me an impression of instability. I feared that in adversity he might fail to stand by, simply because it would bore him beyond words. He seemed to lack solidity, and as I had grown very fond of him I thought it would be better from the point of view of study, and my peace of mind, if we both went our separate ways. I suppose it was the streak of sentimentality in me that made me want to remember our days together at sea as something unspoilt, and in addition, I did not want to become too fond of him. But how to part from him without appearing ungrateful I did not know.

"Look, Peter," I said. "Let's call it a day. We've had a marvellous time on the voyage. But let's leave it at that. I've got to get my nose down to work, and you are going away—so let's say good-bye and have done."

"For goodness sake, woman! Can't I even give you a ring or take you to a show some time? There's no harm in that, is there?"

"No—no, I suppose not, but I'll be busy and you'll have other friends . . ." The argument continued until I began to think I should never leave the platform of the station.

Something must be agreed upon. "Oh well," I said, "New Zealand House will have my address because all my mail will be forwarded from there. Give them a ring, if, and when, you want to."

We embraced and parted.

Chapter 2

PRELUDE TO ANOTHER
JOURNEY

‹‒‒‒‒wwꙊꙊ⦿ꙊꙊwww‒‒‒›

I found a cheerful, middle-aged taxi-driver who, with the
assistance of a porter, put all my trunks in his cab.
"Where to, miss?"

"Please," I said, "don't think I'm mad because I haven't
actually any place to go. I've never been in London before, and
I was hoping that you would be able to tell me where I could
find accommodation for a week or so, at a hostel or a respectable boarding house."

"Colonial, miss?"

"Yes—New Zealander."

"Job, or pleasure?"

"Student."

"Good oh, miss. Me own daughter's goin' in for this study
business. I know just the place. 'Spose you'd like to be sorta
central?"

"Yes, thank you."

London was large, it was alive, but it was not, as I had been
led to believe, lonely. My taxi-driver pulled up outside a tall
building in Holborn.

"This is for young ladies, miss. I think it's what'll suit."

The luggage unloaded, I turned to thank him and pay him.
Then I remembered about tipping, and as I had no idea how
much he expected or merited I asked him. He not only answered my query but also explained that the amount I should
give varied according to the fare charges: he then proceeded to
tell me what the usual amounts were.

I booked in at the hostel for two weeks. As I was too late for

13

the evening meal I wandered down the street in search of a tea-house, taking precautions as I went to make landmarks that I could define even in darkness. I did not want to go too far afield on foot, so I entered a small place although it seemed to be packed with eating people. I sat down at the only vacant table, ordered a pot of tea, and some Welsh Rarebit. As I ate I planned what I should do. My immediate plan was to go to a concert, but I had to find out where to go, and how to get there. My reflections were suddenly interrupted:

"I say, do you mind if I sit at your table? It appears to be the only one left with any room."

I looked up. Standing with his hand on the back of the chair opposite me was a young man, tall, fair, and fresh-complexioned, and from what knowledge I had of my own appearance he was a male duplicate of me. For a few seconds I could do no more than gape owlishly at him before recollecting myself.

"No," I said; "no, that will be quite all right."

We ate in silence. I was wondering if the system for tipping taxi-drivers could be successfully applied to waitresses, for I was still most embarrassed about it. However, the very fact that I realized a waitress ought to be tipped meant that I was adapting myself to English customs. Then I kicked myself mentally for being such an ass: the answer sat opposite me. I had only to wait until he got up, see how much he had left, and leave the same amount myself. As soon as he had gone, I leant across the table, lifted up his cup and saucer, and began shifting back some pennies to count the silver underneath.

A hand closed over my wrist, and a cool, cultured voice said, "Actually—I left that for the waitress . . ."

I have never felt so hot, not even after two games of hockey in one afternoon. People were looking, some with amusement, others with scandalized surprise at what they considered audacious theft. I snatched my hand away, fumbled in my purse for half a crown, put it down beside my plate, and said, "Please come outside, and I'll explain."

Out in the street I fanned my face with my hand and offered my explanation and my apologies.

14

"You say you've only just arrived?" he asked.

"Yes."

"I suppose it is none of my business, but you really shouldn't be roaming around London on your own, you know."

Oh, no, I thought, not another one! I proffered my customary plea for independence, but he still looked dubious.

"My name," he said, "is Gregory Richardson Alverton-Young—a shocker, but Gray for short. I am, I think, sound in wind, limb, and morals, and I know my London. Is there any way in which it would be possible to help you?"

I thanked him, told him my name, and asked him if by any chance he knew where I could go to hear some music. He gave me such a puzzled look that I began to think I must have committed another blunder.

"Whatever is wrong?"

He thrust his hands in his pockets and took two or three paces up and down the street. "Well, you see, I was rather startled when I first saw you, because you could easily pass as my twin sister, and by the expression on your face I gather that you noticed it too?"

I nodded.

"And now you ask me if I can advise you about hearing some music. What kind do you mean?"

"Oh, an orchestral concert, piano or violin recital, or some such."

He pulled a small book out of his pocket. "Look at this." He turned back the front cover, and on it was a stamp bearing the name of the Royal College of Music, London. "I'm a student there—engaged at the moment in orchestral composition, and tonight I am going to the Wigmore Hall to hear some chamber music."

It was bewildering.

"How about coming along to that? I am meeting some other students—we've all got seats together, but I'm sure I'd be able to get you a single somewhere."

I shrugged aside my mother's warnings about casual male acquaintances, and accepted Gray's offer. Riding in a double-decker omnibus for the first time in my life, I was unable to refrain from hugging myself. I wanted to laugh out loud. London was lovely; so was the concert; and so were Gray's friends, especially one, a vivacious girl from Kent. She was a cellist, and invited me to her home in the country any week-end I cared to go. We came out of Wigmore Hall into the heliotrope of an English twilight, found somewhere to have supper, and talked. I counted myself lucky to have found such friends in such a short time, even if they had been acquired by virtue of a little sleight of hand in a tea-house.

My back began to nag that night and I was unable to sleep, but I dismissed it next morning as a chill and went out into an English Sunday, filled with sunshine. I walked in English parks and thought how beautiful they must be in spring. I saw the changing of the guard, visited Madame Tussaud's, and went to a symphony concert in the Albert Hall.

While I was at the concert my back began to ache so badly that I could scarcely attend to the music. The collar of my coat felt very tight and heavy on my neck.

I took two aspirins and went to bed, to spend a miserable night, very cold and in much pain. There was an organ grinder, with a number of notes missing in his grind, playing down in the street directly below my window. Ordinarily I think I should have looked upon him as something quite essential to the romance and atmosphere of London. That night I wished him in merry hell. It was useless lying in bed, so as soon as it was light I had a bath, attempted to unpack my cases, and re-member what it was that I had planned to do. It was a glorious day: but I was cold.

I dressed in the warmest tweeds I had, put on my heavy coat and picked up my clothes brush preparatory to giving myself a final whisk over before setting forth. To my surprise I could not bend my neck, so I stood in front of the wardrobe mirror in my room and brushed my reflection. I thought the sunshine would work wonders. I had not touched any food since midday Sunday, but I did not feel like eating, so thought I was better without it. I was tired beyond words, but I managed to drag myself over to New Zealand House and up the stairs to the mail-room. There was dear old Stephen. I could have hugged him. His smile of greeting quickly gave way to an expression of concern.

"June! Whatever is wrong with you? You look just about all in."

"I think I've caught a chill or something." I sat down on a chair. "Might be homesickness."

"You're in pain, aren't you? Not your back again?"

"Yes, and a splitting head."

"Have you seen a doctor?"

"Oh, Stephen, I can't be bothered. It will pass."

"Look, old girl, I think you'd better go right back to wherever you're staying and I'll send a doctor to you."

I was too tired to argue, so I gave him my address: then I remembered about sending a cable to my people. The lady in the mail-room volunteered to attend to that for me, and Stephen took me down the stairs and hailed a taxi. As I climbed in, he said, "I'm off to Cambridge in half an hour, so I'll have to say good-bye, but please write and let me know how you are."

"I shall, Stephen, and thanks. Cheerio."

Back at the hostel, I undressed slowly, gave myself a severe talking to, and went to have another bath because it seemed to be the only way to keep warm. My neck was as stiff as a board, the pain in my back growing worse, and I wished my head would develop a crater so that I could eject some of the scorching bricks in it. As I came back from the bath clinging to the wall of the passage-way, a little Irish domestic, with a burn scar completely covering one half of her face, came and supported me on one side.

"Feeling faint, miss?"

"No, a bit tired and back-achy—that's all."

"Well, you get to bed, miss, and I'll bring you a nice cuppa tea and a hotty."

"Thanks awfully. Don't think I could take the tea, but I should appreciate the hot-water bottle."

I lay down on my bed, on my stomach, but was smartly on my feet again. Thank heaven there was a wash-basin in my room because I could not have reached the door before I began vomiting. There was a tap at the door and the Irish maid appeared.

"Oh, you poor dear," she said. "What can I do for you?"

"If you could find my warm pyjamas and bed-jacket, I'd be grateful. I'm freezing. I think they're in the middle-sized brown case. Sorry—but I daren't move."

I was sitting in a chair with my head over the basin. She found them, and very slowly, and very carefully, I put them on. Then I took the hot-water bottle, tying it against my back with a thick rug.

Apparently Stephen had not wasted any time, for a doctor soon arrived. My plight, if anything, was worse. He was a thin old man with tired eyes, but a smile which only comes after years of self-sacrifice have moulded its kindliness.

"Well, my dear, where is the trouble?"

"My back principally, doctor."

"Aching?"

"Badly."

"Where?"

"All the way down."

"When, and where, did it start?"

"About two nights ago, at the back of my neck and across my shoulders."

"Spreading downwards?"

"Yes."

"Any other symptoms, apart from vomiting?"

"A frightful head—and a stiff neck."

"I suppose you can't leave that basin?"

"I think it wiser not to."

"Excuse me, I'll be back." He went out the door to reappear about five minutes later with an enamel basin which he placed at the head of the bed. "Now I think you will be safe enough. Just lie on your stomach, will you."

It seemed an eternity in terms of pain and nausea before he straightened up from examining me.

"You will have to go to hospital."

Chapter 3

"STEADY ON, OLD GIRL"

"But I'm not ill enough to go to hospital," I said, with astonishment born of disbelief.

The doctor put his hand on my shoulder. "Aren't you, my dear? Well, you go along, and let them be the judge of that."

"How long will I be there?"

The doctor stroked his chin. "It will take them two or three days to find out exactly what is wrong," he said.

"Will they take this pain away?"

"Yes, I should think so." He took three white tablets out of a bottle. "Do you think you could swallow these? I shall go and order an ambulance."

He went out of the door as I was swallowing the tablets. A few seconds later the Irish maid came in, just as the tablets reappeared.

"Oh, dearie," she said, "couldn't the doctor do no good?"

"Hospital," I gulped, as I pulled a blanket around me, for I had begun shaking every time a wave of pain or cold gripped me. While they came alternately life was reasonably normal, but when they struck simultaneously, nausea came with them, and I was carried away in a flood of unreality from which I emerged, exhausted, but grateful.

"I'll be puttin' a few things in a bag for you, dearie."

"Thanks awfully."

She was a friend indeed, this little maid with the scarred face. Not at any stage did she stand helplessly by, wringing her hands. To attempt to direct proceedings was beyond me because I was under the command of pain.

19

"Dearie—'scuse me askin', but wouldn't you be havin' folks?"

"Not here." Even my mother's love and boiled water, I thought wryly, would not stand a chance with whatever had me in its clutches.

The idea of hospital was no longer unreasonable. It seemed my only salvation, and the sooner I was released from pain the better. A second hot-water bottle was placed on my knee and hands were tying back my hair when there was a knock at the door. As I dare not turn round my little stalwart went over to open it. There was a noise of wheels rattling over a floor, feet tramping, and a voice said: "Can you make the trolley?"

I looked up to see two men in ambulance uniform standing at either end of a piece of canvas stretched on four legs. "I can walk. I don't need that thing."

I got up clutching rugs, hotties, and basin, and started groggily for the door.

"Sorry, we've had instructions that you're not to walk." I was lifted onto the trolley. "And for Pete's sake, keep your head still. That's the most important thing, the doc said." They began unwinding rugs from about me, but I clutched wildly at their warmth.

"Please, no—I'm so cold."

"But we've plenty of rugs."

I sat up to assist them.

The man at my back spoke to the one at my feet.

"It's no good, mate, she's determined to move around. Leave her as she is and get going."

He pressed me back onto the stretch of canvas, took the suit-case which the Irish maid handed to him, and started to tow me out the door.

I looked up at a burn-scarred face. "Bless you," I said. I did not even know her name.

The ambulance driver who sat in the back with me was forced to recognize the futility of the doctor's orders about keeping my head still when he saw how necessary it was for me to turn it basinwards at frequent intervals.

A morning ride across London: I could see out of the square

of glass window, and I understood what I saw until I began tunnelling. And that was the beginning of fear. The tunnel in which I found myself resembled a large city sewer, with a stagnant slime about three feet deep in the bottom and a green slippery seaweed-like growth lining its curving walls. It was dark, dank, and cold. I was an oversized, white, naked body, with frantic fingers scrabbling at the slithery weed in an endeavour to prevent myself from sliding into the horror beneath. As I fought to gain a hold, a hollow, mocking laugh ran from the depths of the tunnel. It came at me in waves, rocking from one side to the other and gaining in resonance as my body dragged my upstretched arms and clutching fingers downwards.

"You fiend! You devil!" I screamed. "You are not going to laugh me into that horrible ooze."

I fought until I became aware that I had my arms round something solid and immovable. It was a pair of uniformed knees belonging to the ambulance man.

"Thank God," I gasped, "you're still with me."

"Yes, I'm still here. You're having a rough journey, aren't you, lass? Never mind, we'll soon be there."

Riding in the back of an ambulance, in the company of pain, cold, and nausea, had suddenly become most enjoyable.

Incomprehension clouded in until I became aware of four square walls, a doorway through one of them, and a table with numerous silver trays on it. A gigantic female figure bent over me poking something into my mouth. I recognized a uniform so I supposed I was in hospital. She seemed to be all eyes and voice: her eyes were a long way off, like enormous brown and white discs.

"I'll be back," she said.

I lay there shaking, trying to associate events with reality, but nothing added up.

A hand drew the thermometer out of my mouth, and I caught the glare of distant eyes.

"Have you had this on your hot-water bottle?"

"No." I was furious, but could not even manage to sound indignant, because I was weary beyond belief. I plunged tunnel-wards once more. Out of this hell of slime and fear I heard a voice:

"Steady on, old girl."

Someone was holding my hand in a strong firm grip, and I looked up to see the dark, clever face of a young doctor. A small but neatly made man, he gazed down at me as if he understood the torment and pain that wracked me, and would have lifted the burden of it had it been within his power. I realized that we were moving.

"Where am I?"

He smiled. "At the moment, you are in a lift. You are being taken to another ward where there is a spare bed."

"No, I mean, what hospital is this?"

"St Mary's."

"Will you take this pain away?"

"Actually, I'm not your doctor. I just happened to be in Casualty, and they asked me to stand by."

My unrelenting enemies, pain, cold, and nausea, were beginning to blind me to ordinary events and I was unaware either of entering the ward, or of being transferred from the trolley to a bed. But a blessed warmth was encompassing me, giving flight to my shivering spasms. I was lying under a large steel cradle, the inside of which was lined with light bulbs whose heat radiated comfort to my body. Approaching me was a nurse carrying a basin full of water and what looked like two huge pieces of flannel.

"Ready for a bath?"

"A bath! Oh, nurse, please, please, leave me alone."

"But you've got to have a bath." She removed the cradle. I was too tired to argue and almost too tired to struggle into a sitting position.

"Whatever are you doing? you must lie down."

"But if I've got to bath myself, I've got to sit up."

"Oh, no, you don't—I'm giving you a blanket bath." She began to unfold what I had thought were two pieces of flannel. They were red blankets.

"Please, nurse, let me do it myself. I can't bear to be touched." But my protestation was in vain. That bath was agony: I behaved badly and was ashamed. Dear God! I thought, why don't they stop pulling me about and give me something to stop this pain? I want some sleep . . . perhaps then I can recover my sense of proportion.

There seemed to be a great many people round my bed, most of them in long white coats mouthing long words. One of them, with a stethoscope dangling from his neck, leant towards the locker, which was standing by my bed, and glanced at the basin on it. "Hm—still vomiting." He sounded so jolly about it I felt I could have hit him had I not been utterly worn out.

Things were slipping away again and while I clenched my teeth preparatory to renewing my combat in that damnable tunnel I wondered if I could struggle with it much longer. But it did not last as long this time. One of the bodies in a white coat had put the cradle back on my bed—and as the heat began to penetrate a voice came from a great distance asking me my name.

"June," I said.

"June what?"

To my horror I felt tears spilling out of my closed eyes.

A hand was put over mine. "What is the matter?"

I was at the end of my tether. "I haven't any friends."

"But we're all your friends," the kindly voice insisted.

"Well," I said wearily, "if you're my friends, you must know my other name."

And there the matter rested until Casualty supplied the information they sought.

I was grateful when they left me alone. With no questions to answer and no one to push my sick body about, I was able to rest, if rest it could be called. An explosion seemed about to occur in my head, and it was hopeless to attempt to ease the pain in my back by shifting my position in bed, so I lay there, grateful for the warmth that seeped through me.

I heard a voice call urgently: "Nurse, nurse, come quickly! The new patient's out of bed."

I thought hazily of the ingratitude of people who failed to comply with the commands of doctors and nurses who were doing their utmost to make them better. I became aware that I could see a pair of pink floral pyjama legs beneath me. I'm going silly, I thought . . . those are my legs. Then I realized that I was the patient who was out of bed. I was standing on the lid of my locker. There was a scurry of feet and a gentle voice beseeching me to get back into bed.

"There's nothing for it," a man's voice said, "we shall have to put cot sides on her bed."

The screens were pushed open as I heard a crisp, decisive answer. "No, we shall not. We're not putting cot sides on that girl's bed. I'd rather spare one of my nurses to sit by her." A soothing hand was laid on mine. "Now, my dear, what's all this nonsense about getting out of bed?"

I looked up into a pair of brown eyes sparkling with humour, and understanding. That was the first time I remember seeing the Sister of the ward, and because she had protested against the ignominy of being penned in bed like a lunatic I hung onto her hand in unspoken gratitude as I made my apologies. "There is no need to leave a nurse," I said. "I'll stay in bed."

Amber lights shot into her eyes as she smiled. "Yes. I believe you would." She had my confidence from that moment. Then she looked across my bed at the doctor. "I'll have to send a nurse to her anyway. She's got to be prepared for Doctor Timms."

I grinned up at her.

"Why are you smiling?" asked the doctor.

"Because that statement of Sister's was worthy of a diplomat. She has appeased both you and me while getting on with the business in hand."

He laughed: then enquired hopefully, "Are you feeling better?"

"No, I'm not. But I feel much safer."

They left me to the ministrations of a nurse, whose preparations for the doctor who was coming to examine me consisted of unbuttoning my pyjama coat, rolling up the legs of my pants to above my knees, and turning back the bedclothes at the foot of the bed, leaving my feet exposed.

"Is this doctor somebody important?" I asked, because the

nurse had wheeled a trolley, with a business-like looking array of instruments on it, to the foot of my bed.

"Oh, yes," she said. "He's a neurologist, and Dean of the Medical School. This is his ward."

The screens parted to admit Sister. Without wasting words, she scrutinized the trolley, and then me. "Nurse!" she cried in a tone of horror. "Just look at those feet."

"Sorry, Sister," I said, "it's hopeless. They're really clean."

"Clean? They're black!"

"I know they are. But I played deck games on the ship in my bare feet and the black pitch between the boards is ingrained in my soles. It won't wash off."

Nurse used a crucible of methylated spirits, a clean cloth, and a lot of elbow grease on my feet, but she failed to remove any of the stain. "It's not making any difference," she said, "and I'm getting away from here before they arrive. I can hear Doctor Timms through in the main ward."

As she had left the screens open I was able to see the stone archway opening onto the main ward. Through it streamed a veritable retinue, headed by Sister and a tall erect man in his forties. My first impression of him was one of vigour and competence. He walked swiftly, and with purpose, putting his feet on the ground as if he would always know where he wanted to go and the best way to get there. There was neither a white coat nor a stethoscope dangling from his neck. He read the thermometer which stood in a glass of pink disinfectant on my locker, took my pulse, then looked down at me.

"June, are you too tired to answer some questions? I'll be as quick as I can."

"No," I replied, thinking how kind it was of him to consider whether I was tired or not.

I was surprised to see a grim but determined expression on his face as he bent over me and said: "I've got to examine this back of yours. It won't be pleasant for you."

It was not.

When it was over everyone departed except Sister, Dr Timms, and a dark bespectacled young doctor who had been assiduously scribbling in a notebook whilst the examination was conducted. They held a parley in undertones at the foot of my bed.

Dr Timms turned to me with a smile that was delightful because of its charm, and surprising because it was all too rare.

"I'll see you tomorrow, June." Then to the young doctor. "Try and get her temperature down. And do a lumbar puncture immediately."

They had not been gone long when an exceedingly pretty little nurse arrived inside my screens to tidy me up. She was efficient, but gentle. "What a super tan you've got," she said as she pulled my pyjama coat on.

"I've had a glorious New Zealand summer and a long sea voyage in which to acquire it."

She looked at me somewhat guiltily. "You know, it's hard to believe you're really ill. You look healthier than anyone I've seen for ages . . . Oh, Doctor Black, are you ready to start now?"

"Yes, nurse." It was the voice of Dr Timms's bespectacled aide-de-camp.

Outside the screens I heard Dr Black addressing someone: "I say, old chap, you wouldn't like to do a lumbar puncture for me, would you?"

I groaned inwardly, wondering how many more doctors were going to view me. All I wished was for Dr Black to get this puncturing business over, so that I could be left alone. A white-coated arm pushed back the screens. Then I heard Dr Black's voice:

"Will you chaperone, nurse?"

"Yes, doctor."

Nurse came in, pushing a trolley which was covered with a white cloth. She was followed by Dr Black, who ushered in a man in plain clothes. He was young; he was small, but neatly made; and he had a dark, clever face.

"Hallo," I said, "I'm so glad to see you."

Dr Black raised his eyebrows, and burst out laughing.

"Well," he said, "you are a dark horse, Tommy. I assume you two have met?"

The other smiled. "Yes, we met in the lift—holding hands."

While the plain-clothes doctor was offering an explanation I was silently praying that he would take over the puncturing, or at least, stand by while it was being done.

"Will you take it on?" queried Dr Black, indicating the trolley.

"Oh, look here," the other protested, "I'm on holiday."

Then he looked at me. Verbally I could not beg any favours of him in the presence of another doctor, but I endeavoured, quite shamelessly, to plead with my eyes. He looked away, gave a slightly embarrassed laugh, and started unbuttoning his sports coat. "All right," he said, "I'll do it."

The little man rolled up his shirt-sleeves, then he bent over me with an expression of commiseration on his face. "Look, June," he said, "to do this I've got to have you lying on your side with your knees drawn up to your chin and your back curved. It's about the most painful position I could ask you to adopt. I'm sorry." He turned to the nurse. "Don't make her shift until I've scrubbed up."

When explanations prefix unpleasant but necessary actions one is unafraid, prepared, and able to co-operate. Sister, Dr Timms, the pretty nurse, and this man seemed to possess such understanding and consideration that I was filled with a sudden determination to fight this thing no matter how difficult it became. I pointed to a disappearing back. "What's his name?" I asked Dr Black.

"Tommy Stroobant. He's just completed his six months as a houseman on this ward. That's why I asked him to do your lumbar puncture. He's had plenty of practice. I took over from him today."

Dr Stroobant was back, with arms dripping from above the elbows. With a pair of forceps Nurse dropped a hand-towel on them. He did dry his arms himself, but Nurse held his white gown while he plunged his arms simultaneously through its sleeves. Nurse tied it at the back: she also, with a pair of forceps, uncovered the trolley. I suspected that the next move must be mine, so I rolled onto my side and pulled my knees up to my chin.

"Good girl. Get a firm grip on her knees and shoulders,

nurse, and try and stop as much movement as you can when she starts to retch."

When it was over I rolled onto my back again, straightened my legs, and took a drink of water Nurse was tendering me.

"Was it very bad?" she asked.

"No, I didn't feel the needle going in at all."

Dr Stroobant laughed shortly. "You wouldn't, not with all the other things that must be going on in your back."

"Do you know what is causing the pain?" I looked apprehensively at Dr Stroobant.

His eyes were direct and honest. "No, I don't."

I turned to Dr Black. "Does Doctor Timms know?"

"No, he doesn't know either. That's why he ordered this," indicating the hypodermic syringe full of the fluid that had been drawn from my back.

"Thank you."

They walked to the foot of my bed and together lifted it in the air. "Blocks, nurse!" Nurse pushed something along the floor, they relieved their arms of weight, but my bed remained foot-tilted.

Dr Black spoke. "You'll develop a headache quite soon. It's only caused by loss of pressure as a result of the fluid that has been drawn off. This will help restore it."

He was pointing at the raised bed end.

And that, I decided as they both walked away, was the first really ridiculous remark I had heard since my arrival in hospital, because I believed, with some justification, that I had been prey to an over-developed headache for longer than I cared to remember. I was alone, and I was exasperated beyond measure with this sick body of mine.

I rolled over on my stomach, and although this brought me no relief from pain, it brought my eyes into contact with a brass plaque, which was screwed into the wall directly above the head of my bed. On it was engraved: FRANCES JAYCOX I. My reflections on its origin were cut short by the return of the nurse.

"You've got to have an injection of penicillin, and Sister told me to put this on your back." She pushed something that felt like a square of flannelette on my back, poked an electric plug in the wall, and a needle into my arm.

"Nurse, who is, or was, Frances Jaycox the first?"

Nurse laughed. "That doesn't mean 'the first'—that means bed number one."

"But who is she, and what's this brass plate for?"

"Some old girl who donated so many thousands for a bed in the hospital. If you contribute a certain amount you get your name on the wall—in brass. She must have given a whale of a sum, because there are three brass plates with her name on them."

"Good gracious! She's dead, I suppose?"

"Yes, of course."

"Did she die in this bed? What a horrid thought."

Nurse burst into shrieks of laughter. "I don't know whether she did or not, but most beds in a hospital have had dead bodies in them at some time or another, you know."

I was endeavouring to keep my thoughts on Frances Jaycox when Dr Black and Dr Stroobant appeared behind the screens.

"We have come to see how your head is," said Dr Black.

"Well actually, doctor, it's feeling better than it's felt for days."

"What?" They both looked and spoke their surprise.

"It's true. . . . I've had a wretched headache for ages, and this is the first time I've felt it lifting at all."

"Well, I'll be damned! But you know it is possible, I suppose." Dr Black spoke to his companion. "In the ordinary course of events patients get headaches because of loss of cerebro-spinal fluid, and consequently pressure. On the other hand, if the patient already has a snorter of a headache, pressure must be increased already and the drawing off of C.S.F. could relieve it."

I had ceased worrying about the causes for things: effects were all important. My headache was decidedly easier and I was kept warm. All day I lay in hope. It was not a bad day, all things considered, because I had become habituated to the basin business, there were no more examinations or people to push my tortured body about, and I only tunnelled once.

By nightfall my optimism was beginning to flag, and my most vivid recollection of the night was of my own misconduct and arrant cowardice, and of the nurse, whose patience must have been sorely tried, but who never once upbraided me. The bed seemed to be too small and I became helplessly entangled in blankets as I thrashed about wrestling with pain. The light burning above me hurt my eyes, so I switched it off. Nurse switched it on, only to find it off again as soon as her back was turned. We had several battles over that light switch. I complained about my back, and queried the reason for my presence in a hospital when they were not doing anything to give me relief. I wanted sleep more than I had ever wanted anything in my life. I asked God to send sleep to me: I asked Nurse to give me something to put me to sleep: I talked to Frances Jaycox about it.

Nurse said, "I'll send for Sister."

"Oh, yes nurse, please do." But when she came she was a stranger. "You're not the Sister I want," I said.

"I'm the Night Sister."

"Where is the one that was here when I came in?"

"She's off duty, in bed and asleep, I hope. We can't keep going for twenty-four hours, my dear."

"Sorry . . . Sister, can I please have something to put me to sleep?"

"Bring her a couple of aspirins, nurse."

I laughed in her face, and was bewildered by my own behaviour.

"Why are you laughing like that?" she said.

"Nothing." My voice was nasty, and I wondered why I was being so rude. Nurse brought me the aspirins, which I swallowed, but which reappeared before Sister had left my bed.

"Oh," she said. "Ring Casualty for a doctor, nurse."

He was not long in coming, and my humiliation at my own unreasonable behaviour was deepened when I saw who it was. "Doctor Stroobant," I whispered.

He did not mince matters. "You want some sleep, my dear? Well, I'll be perfectly frank with you." He put a cool hand on my head. "I feel a beast because you have got to go on with

30

this. We cannot take away the symptoms of a disease until that disease has been diagnosed. Yours hasn't been—and as this back of yours is the main symptom, we can't do away with it just yet. We ought to have the result of that fluid test in a few hours, and then, perhaps, something can be done."

"Why didn't someone tell me all this?" I asked. "I'm sorry, and I'll try not to make any more fuss."

That was at two o'clock in the morning. At ten he was back, to be greeted with pleased surprise by Dr Black and the Day Sister, who were, at that moment, by my bedside. "I thought you were on holiday?" I said.

"So did I," put in Dr Black.

Dr Stroobant grinned ruefully at his fellow. "Oh, I did a night on Cas for Worthington. He has flu."

Dr Black came close. "Roll over," he said. There was a sharp jab in my seat. As I twisted onto my back again, they were going out of the screens. Dr Stroobant looked back.

"Sweet dreams," he said.

I silently commended them on their astuteness. A quick word, a smart action, and they had gone. I gathered that I had been given something to make me sleep which meant, I suspected, that they had made their diagnosis. But unanswered questions troubled me not: the cursed pain was flowing out of my body. I thought that I had never known such happiness. I shut my eyes and slept.

I awoke, clapped my hands to my eyes, and screamed. Someone came running.

"Whatever is the matter?" said the voice of the pretty nurse. "You mustn't make a noise like that."

"Oh, nurse," I moaned, "I thought the roof was falling in on me."

A hand that I knew gripped mine and a voice that I was coming to love said: "June, you are quite all right. Open your eyes, and look at me."

I looked up. "Oh, Sister," I said, "I was so frightened."

She smiled. "Ring for two orderlies, nurse. We'll have her moved into the main ward where I can keep my eye on her."

31

They moved the bed, with me in it, into a much larger ward where there seemed to be quite a number of other patients whose voices came through the screens, and whose one topic of conversation was food. I sat up to grab my basin. To my complete amazement I remained lying flat on my back, but a basin I must have, so I called Nurse. Sister came, took in the situation at a glance, and attended to my needs.

"Sister," I said when it was all over, "such a funny thing's happened. I can't sit up. I never knew anyone could get as weak as that just because they hadn't eaten for a few days."

"Didn't you, my dear?" She turned quickly and left me.

A few minutes later there was the sound of many tramping feet, voices murmuring, and I saw Dr Timms's face above the screens. He looked over at me, smiled, then came in.

"How are you, June?"

"Fine, thanks."

Bodies were pushing their way through the screens. A voice said: "Lecture, sir?"

"No . . . and no one is to worry the patient with questions or examinations." He turned to me. "Will you try and sit up, just once, when I give you the word?"

"Yes, certainly."

He knelt down on the floor at the head of my bed. "Right—now!" My brain obeyed his command, but not my body. "Thank you," he said, as he stood upright.

I dared not ask him what was in my mind. Everyone seemed to regard him with a respectful silence which I was afraid it was not my place to interrupt. What he wanted to divulge he would, when he considered it advisable.

As the day progressed I found it increasingly difficult to grasp the fact that I was really myself, or that anything was what it appeared to be. Had it not been for the frequent appearances of Sister, Dr Black, and Dr Stroobant, I think I should have succeeded in my belief that I existed only in a world of unreality, from which I should waken to a state of body and mind that was normal, and therefore, credible. But because I knew these people were real, I had to condition myself to accept the strange things that were taking place as real also,

32

and then to adjust myself to them. At some stage during the afternoon I discovered that I could not roll over in bed. I did not like it, and was frightened.

With the coming of the night my hands lay idle, ceasing to obey my will. I hated that, and was terrified.

The night was one of fluctuating periods of comprehensibility and incomprehensibility, both of which were hell because they intensified fear. My tunnelling ceased, only to make way for another kind of horror. I lay, enormous and naked, across the sharp-lipped crater of a mountain. I was as light as air. The mountain was high, and bare, surrounded by a dusty arid plain . . . everything was brown. A faint whistling sound and a dust cloud advanced across the plain together, the one gaining in intensity and the other in density, as they reached the foot of the mountain. The whistle rose in a crescendo that ended in a wild screech as the cloud slowly rose to envelop me . . . but always there was a firm hand grip and a voice, saying, "Steady on, old girl."

"I'm frightened, Doctor Stroobant—terribly frightened."

"I know you are. But hang on—you'll be all right."

"Will this ever stop?"

"Yes, it must."

Morning came at last, and with it the strength of Sister's presence.

"May I see the patient, Sister?" It was the voice of the doctor who had sounded so jolly about my vomiting. I had no desire to see him.

"Yes, certainly, doctor."

The screens opened to admit one of the handsomest men I had ever seen. He took one step towards the locker.

"Good heavens! You're not still vomiting?"

He did not sound at all jolly about it this morning, but the evidence was there, and he turned a concerned face to Sister as she came in. "Sister, can't we do anything to stop this?"—indicating the basin. I felt myself warming to him.

"We've tried everything, but she can't keep anything down long enough for it to be of any benefit."

"There must be some way of stopping it." His voice was so

genuinely distressed that I scored out my first impression of him, and put him in the category of the considerate and understanding.

"Well——" Sister hesitated. "Could we try a binder? It's an old-fashioned idea, but it may work."

"By all means—do." While Sister was away the doctor stood and looked at me. He had a wide smile that went well with his handsome face. "The devil of it is, you know," he said wryly, "you look so healthy."

I was beyond caring how I looked. Sister returned with masses of cotton-wool, bandages, and strips of stiff cardboard. From this they together fashioned a large flat pad, which they strapped across my stomach, then pulled as tightly as they could, before tying it. We all waited until time gave us conclusive proof. It worked. My gratitude to Sister was unspoken and unbounded. Cold, pain, and nausea were being kept in abeyance and I was left only with fear, which was never as bad when Sister was near.

It reached its peak in the afternoon. I dreamt that I was drowning, being drawn further and further down in the depths of a dirty bottomless river. I was terrified and struggled against the downward pull: but it was too powerful. At last, in the silt and swirling water, I choked . . .

Sister was tugging at my hand when I opened my eyes. "What happened, June?"

I was gasping. "I dreamt I was drowning, Sister. It was awful."

She did not appear to be paying much attention to what I was saying as she released my hand, turned quickly from my bed, and disappeared through the gap between the screens. I felt rebuked. She returned in a little while with Dr Timms, who uttered but a curt word of greeting as he bent over me with a watch in his hand. I was still gasping.

"Don't talk, June—just lie there."

He stood over my body for some considerable time before they both left me. Their silence was bewildering. A nurse came and was going through a temperature-pulse routine, made difficult by my shuddering breath, when I heard something,

34

which sounded very heavy and cumbersome, being trundled into the ward.

Nurse peered over the screen. "Oh," was all she said.

"Open the screens, please, nurse."

She did so, to disclose a number of young men, some nurses, Dr Timms, Dr Black, and Sister, pushing a huge white box on wheels which they jockeyed about until it stood parallel with my bed. It was a hideous thing, looking unpleasantly like a coffin mounted on four legs. A big oblong box, all closed up: then I saw the hole in the top end of it. A hole about the size of a person's neck. "Oh, God," I prayed, almost aloud, "don't let them put me in that. Please God! I'd die in that box."

There was a tramp of retreating feet: then silence. I looked at the two people standing by my bed. Dr Timms sat down beside me.

"June," he said, in a voice so kind and gentle that I could guess what he had to say, "I'm afraid you will have to be put in that."

"No," I whispered. "Please, no."

"We wouldn't do it, if we didn't have to."

"But why?"

"It will do your breathing for you, until you are strong enough to manage it yourself."

"I can breathe."

"Now, my dear, you know perfectly well that every breath you draw is an effort, and a greater one, every time."

The rapid rasping noise I was making was sufficient evidence for that, but I was dogged by fear. "Sister," I gasped, "please don't let him put me in that."

Sister took my hand firmly in both of hers, "It is for your own safety, my dear."

Dr Timms got to his feet. "I'll get Black, and Stroobant," he said to Sister; "don't leave her."

"No, please don't leave me, Sister. I'm so frightened."

"Don't talk, June. Try and save your breath. I'll stay with you, for as long as you want me. And you've got to be a sensible girl, and a brave girl, and let Doctor Timms put you in. I know you're exhausted, and you're in pain, and you're badly frightened, but you will help yourself, and all of us who want to see you well again, if you do as Doctor Timms asks and be brave about it."

I thought what a beastly coward I had just proved myself to be, and was ashamed, but I felt panic rising again as the effort to draw a breath reached the stage where it almost exhausted me. I dare not speak to Sister but she bent over me and said quietly:

"Take it as easily as you can, and concentrate everything you've got on your breathing."

It was fear at its worst. Nebulous discs of black, then red, swimming towards me out of a mist, a deafening noise, and through it all a faint voice saying: "Careful with her arms and legs—I'll take her head." I was catapulting through space, spinning wildly: then I became conscious that I was taking in great gulps of air. I was alone: lying on a steep hill head downwards, but I could breathe again—and breathe freely.

Thus I passed from April into May.

Chapter 4

INTO UNCERTAIN LIGHT

igh up through a square of glass, at the top of a
window, I could see a patch of blue that was the sky.
I'll let one more cloud go past, I thought, before
forcing my attention back to myself, an unpleasant subject for
contemplation, but one that must be confronted. The temptation to prolong the respite proved irresistible, and five more
clouds scudded by before I brought my thoughts to heel. I
shut my eyes the better to concentrate.

I must deal with the present first of all. The past, if it was to
be of any use, would fall into line as I went along: the future,
temporarily, must be left to itself. I was in the box—of that I
was certain. I was also certain, as well as happily surprised,
that it was neither painful nor frightening. There were two
extraordinary and penetrating noises keeping pace with each
other. One seemed to issue from the box, the other from me.
At least they've got rhythm if they've got nothing else, I
thought. Then I focused all my mental powers on solving the
riddle of what lay inside the box, for there was no doubt that
it belonged to me. Of that I was gratefully aware, but I had to
find out what had happened to it.

Starting at my feet I worked slowly upwards, carefully test-
ing every portion of my body for signs of movement. I sometimes found myself drifting away with weariness, for it was a
long, exhaustive self-examination: toes, feet, knees, legs, hips,
bottom, stomach, back, chest, shoulders, arms, hands, fingers.
Nothing moved. There was no pause for lamentations, or
queries, no time for fear. If this was something which had to
be fought, I must assess the total damage, so that I knew what
had been left of me with which to fight it. Obviously what was

37

inside the box was, at the moment, dead, and must be dismissed . . . but what of that which was outside?

Driven on beyond weariness, I tried to move my neck, but that was caught fast in some sort of collar. I tried my jaw—it moved. I could not lift my head, or turn it sideways, but I could blink what I imagined were both my eyelids, and I could hear. I could see quite clearly when I looked to the left, or straight ahead, but a blurred arc of confused objects was all that met me when I turned my eyes to the right. To the left was the patch of blue which was my haven. Straight ahead of me was the upper half of a steel girdle, about a foot wide, which was part of the collar encircling my neck. The collar separated my head from my body: the living from the dead. I had discovered what I had to know, so I shut my eyes and left it at that.

Something was being poked up one of my nostrils. I opened my eyes in stupefaction not untinged with indignation.

"Hallo," said a surprised but soft voice, from somewhere behind my head.

"Arrh," was my reply. I was astounded, because what I had meant to say was, "Hallo." My first thought, that I had lost the power of speech, was frightening. My second, that my family would never believe such a thing, was rueful, and it pulled me up short. The past leapt suddenly into focus. My family: my mother, my father, and my sister in New Zealand—what did they know of me? What could they know of me? I had been too ill to send a cable, I remembered.

"June, can't you see me?"

My bewildered thoughts swivelled back to the present. "Arrh," I said.

The thing was withdrawn from my nostril, there was a rustling movement, and I saw the head and shoulders of a nurse. What I could see of her face was pale, but conveyed little, for she was wearing a gauze mask. A white starched cap sat well back on her soft brown hair, her eyes were grey and smiling, and two thin strips of white disappeared behind her ears, coming together in a stiff white bow under her mask. That bow fascinated me because it looked stupidly out of place. Silly bit of professional clobber, I thought, and looked away to those smiling eyes. "Can you see me, now?"

"Arrh."

She was looking at me in some perplexity. "Look, we'll tackle this speech business later. Can you wink?"

I batted my left eyelid.

"Splendid. We'll manage with that for the present. When you want to say 'yes', you wink that eye, and when you want to say 'no', leave it open—got it? Now, can you see me?"

I winked at her.

She moved. "Can you see me, here?" Nothing but a blur, so I kept my eye open. "Here?" My eye remained open. "Here?" I winked quickly, twice. She was under the patch of sky. She moved about questioning me, but always, when she came into that position, I winked twice, and rapidly.

"Right," she said. "I get you. You can see me best when I stand here?" She was leaning over the corner of the box nearest my left eye.

I winked, and silently commended her for her perspicacity. She remained where she was.

"I'm your nurse," she said. "My name is Joyce Farley. You are in a small room, in St Mary's Hospital, and you're in an iron lung. I'm with you all the time during the day, except when I go off for meals, and then another nurse comes to relieve me. You have a special night nurse who has a relief also. You are never left alone, so there is no need ever to be frightened. Got that?"

I winked.

"We'll gradually get things sorted out . . . and now, I shall have to leave you while I go and telephone. I'll send another nurse along to be with you." She moved out of sight.

There is really no need to send anyone else, I thought, as nothing can possibly happen to me.

Then I heard Nurse Farley's voice: "Stand by the top left-hand corner of the lung, nurse. She can see you there."

Despite gauze trappings and starched cap the expression on the face that now appeared was undisguisedly one of terror. Her eyes were riveted on my face. You poor kid, I thought, you're scared stiff! We gazed at each other, warily, like two dogs, and I was just wondering whether a wink would ease the tension when I saw her look up. The relief that flooded her eyes was pathetic proof that my own nurse had returned.

When she came into view over the corner of the box—or lung, as I now knew it—Nurse Farley was rolling a piece of cotton-wool round one end of a thin wooden stick about six inches long. "June, this is to clean your nose." She held up the stick. "I do it twice a day. I had just begun this morning when you woke up. You've no idea how startled you looked . . . but I'll explain everything as I go along." She probed about inside my nostrils. Even had I been able to speak, my humiliation was beyond expressing.

"Mm," I said.

She looked up quickly. "Hallo—new noise. But don't struggle with your speech just yet. I'll finish this, and then, if you are not too tired, we'll see what can be done. But you've got to take everything in easy stages, because you'll tire quickly."

For the first time Nurse had jumped to the wrong conclusion, but I had let it pass, as there was no way of explaining that I had only been trying to blow my nose.

She moved away and back again, re-wrapping the stick before operating on my other nostril. During this excavation I heard footsteps approaching at a pace that was nearer a gallop than a walk. They halted, not very far away. Nurse looked up.

"Oh, doctor—could you fix your own mask, please? You'll find one in the drum behind the door. I want to finish this."

"Yes, certainly," replied a voice that I knew but could not place.

Withdrawing the stick, Nurse straightened up. "Come and stand here, where I am. She can see you best in this position."

One face replacing another, and masked as the second was there was no mistaking the brown-eyed, bespectacled Dr Black. "Well! This is grand, June, isn't it?"

I winked.

A dull red rose above the mask, and his eyes shifted. My amazement, as I realized that he was acutely embarrassed by such unexpected behaviour, was unbounded, and quite without pity, because as soon as his eyes came back to my face I winked again. His discomfort increased.

"Um . . . nurse?"

"Yes, doctor?" It was a splutter of sound from behind me, followed by a low peal of laughter. Nurse Farley, I thought, you're a smart girl. You've missed nothing.

"Look here—what are you two up to? Is this a conspiracy?"

"No. Sorry, doctor. It's our system of communication. That wink means 'yes', not . . . not . . ." and Nurse was off again.

Dr Black was frowning. "But, nurse, seriously . . . I don't understand. Can't she talk?"

"I don't know. She's made some funny sounds, so there's something there."

"But she ought to be able to talk. I'm pretty sure of that."

I put a halter on excitement because I wanted proof.

My brain was going round in circles by the time I had followed all their conversation and carried out their instructions. The fault, I gathered, lay not in me but in the box. Attached to the end of the lung was a long, fat, hose-like piece of tubing. Somewhere along this was a huge contraption, resembling fireside bellows, from which a further length of tubing led to an electric plug in the wall. With the turning of a switch the bellows worked in exactly the same manner as they would to create a fire draught. They pushed and sucked air in and out of the lung at intensely high pressure, sufficient to flatten the whole of my chest wall for expiration, and to release it for inhalation. As the air pressed down against my body my ribs were forced inwards, and air came rushing out of my mouth. As the pressure was released so my ribs and lungs expanded, causing air to be sucked down through my mouth. Thus, I breathed.

The pressure and rate of breathing was adjustable. Once the tempo was set, the lung maintained a steady, continual pumping movement on my body. The noise of the bellows could be heard above all else: a noise like steam escaping from a railway engine, except that it was a rhythmical "hiss, hiss", which never ceased. Keeping pace with this hissing was a guttural sizzle which came from my mouth, caused by the outward and inward rushing of my breath.

While air was being sucked down my throat, speech was impossible—it would have been impossible for anyone—so we concentrated on making something intelligible come through the sizzle of exhalation. After much trial and error, the first faint sounds issued. I waited for an outrush of air. "Nurse Farley," I shouted quickly. It came as a whisper; but it came.

Dr Black put his hand on my head. "Well done! You have a rest, while I talk to Nurse."

I looked up to the top of the window. I could hear; I could see, if only with one eye; and I could speak, in spasms. That was all I asked of life at that moment.

Some time later I became aware of a sharp jabbing sensation in my left arm. What it was that jabbed, I did not question, because the knowledge that I could feel absorbed all thought. I opened my eyes to find Nurse Farley leaning over the left-hand corner of the lung, her eyes fixed intently on its flat top, and her body pressed against its side. I waited until I felt air pouring out of my mouth: "Nurse Farley?"

She looked up quickly. "Sorry, June. Did I wake you?"

I made a spluttering noise before recollecting that, insofar as speech was concerned, I was the servant of an extraordinary master who did not permit a continuous flow of intelligible sound to escape from me. I waited, literally, until I had got my breath before hissing out the only thing of importance at that moment. "I can feel."

"Feel what?"

"Something in. . . ." A plague on this short-circuiting, I thought, wearily . . . "my arm."

Nurse bent nearer. "What sort of thing?"

"A jab."

"That's splendid. That was me, giving you an injection. Doctor Timms was up during the morning, while you were asleep, and he wanted to know if you could feel."

"Sorry."

"Sorry? Why?"

"Missed him."

Nurse laughed. "So was he—sorry he missed speaking to you. He wouldn't disturb you, but he was practically willing you to wake up. He'll be back, though. He wants you to try and learn to swallow."

I was rapidly adopting a manner of speaking which put my thoughts into as few words as possible. "Baby," I said.

"What baby?" Nurse's voice held an inflection of astonishment.

"Me, learning . . . to swallow."

The grey eyes smiled. "There's no mistaking you for a baby. You've got the constitution of an ox, and not a baby one, either. Doctor Timms said, to start off with——"

She stopped abruptly as a knock sounded somewhere to the right of me. She moved quickly out of sight, and I heard her conversing in low tones to whoever it was who had knocked. There were footsteps, which were not hers, coming nearer.

"The top left-hand corner. She'll see you best there."

I could not believe what I saw above that gauze mask, but a hand was on my cheek conveying more than the voice, that said: "Hullo, Swan."

"Peter!"

He let me recover before he spoke again. "Sorry, my dear, I suppose I came as a bit of a shock to you?"

"How——"

"Did I know? Look, Swan, don't you talk. Nurse says I'm not to tire you, but I'll endeavour to bring you up to date as best I can, in the time allowed. . . . First, there's your family. They know—through the New Zealand High Commissioner. He sent them a cable, as soon as he knew—the hospital got in touch with him—and there's one been sent, every day since. I've written to your mother and tried to explain things to her. They've written from New Zealand House, and also from St Mary's, so don't worry on that score. I've been to the hostel where you were staying and collected all your gear. It's packed, and stored, in New Zealand House. A little Irish maid helped me—one with a badly scarred face—she asked after you. We found a list of all your clothes, so we were able to check everything. It's all intact."

To smother my amazement, completely, was impossible. My mind would flit off at tangents, thinking of my father, who had insisted that I make an inventory of my clothes before I packed, and my reluctance to do so; the Irish maid who again had cause to be blest; and the New Zealand High Commissioner who was unknown to me but who had apparently been very active on my behalf. And through it all, was Peter.

"There's quite a bundle of mail for you, at New Zealand House. I'll bring it over tomorrow and read it to you."

Out of a confused maze of thought I remembered that Peter was supposed to be going to Italy.

"Italy?" I queried.

His eyes came back to my face and he shrugged slightly. "Oh, I've postponed my trip for a while."

"Peter, when . . ."

"Is she all right, nurse?"

"Yes. She has to talk in spasms, that's all. You'll have to learn to wait for the bits and string them together yourself."

"I see. Go on, Swan. 'When' what?"

"Did you first . . . see me?"

He looked away and said quickly, "Please, don't let us go into that." I was horrified to see tears in his eyes.

As he stood there, I remembered my previous judgement of him. It seemed he had sacrificed a great deal, and done much to help a friend in adversity. "Peter?"

"Yes?"

"You've been . . . wonderful."

"Fiddlesticks!" There was a hint of his old impatience, then a smile, in his eyes. "You've set a pretty high standard in that direction yourself."

I had done nothing but pick up a bug.

"Nurse is pointing at the door, so I must go. I'll be back, tomorrow. This has been a red-letter day. Don't worry about anything. It will sort itself out. Good-bye, my dear."

"Good-bye . . . and thanks." There was too much to be sorted out: a chaos of fast moving and quickly changing thoughts careered through my head.

44

"Why the ponderous frown?" Nurse Farley had returned from seeing Peter off.

"There's too much . . . to think about."

"Now look, June." She spoke sternly. "All you have got to think about is yourself. I know you can't dismiss other things altogether, but you're not to worry over them. Your friend, Peter, has done everything possible to relieve you of worry; the New Zealand High Commissioner keeps in constant touch with us, and your parents, so you just concentrate on getting yourself better. That's your principal job, at the moment . . . and if you don't wipe that frown away, I shall have to stop Peter Johns from visiting you."

From that moment, I decided, if somewhat callously, that I must leave the outside world alone, in order to pit all my strength and thought against that dead body inside the lung. I owed something to these people who were standing by, and I could not hope to repay my debt to them by prolonged mmobility and helplessness.

"Nurse, when can . . . we start this . . . swallowing?"

"As soon as you've had a rest. It's three o'clock now. We'll say four, for our first experiment. Try and sleep."

A few minutes after four a stream of orange juice was ejected from my mouth, like water from a siphon, finding a target in the centre of Nurse Farley's white starched apron-bib.

"Sorry, nurse."

"That's all right. I know you're not spitting on me purposely. This is going to take some working out. I think I'd better move out of range—I'll stand directly behind your head and drop it in from there."

She had squeezed the juice of an orange into a tumbler, which she held in her left hand while with her right she endeavoured, by means of a teaspoon, to drop small portions of the liquid into my gaping mouth. This was well planned, well timed, and most successful; but what happened to that orange juice after it dropped to the back of my throat was unexpected, most untimely, and very messy. Nurse wisely decided to waste such precious fluid no longer. "We'll try some water, June."

"All right." The skin on my face felt tight with a sticky sweetness.

We were most abandoned. Nurse experimented with large quantities and small, with a rapid succession of loaded spoonfuls and with tiny drops a considerable interval apart. She dropped it right into the back of my throat and on the tip of my tongue, then she tried slipping it craftily down the inside of my cheek. It was of no avail. Water sprayed everywhere, joining the sticky rivulets of orange juice.

"You're having a royal clean-up, if nothing else. I give up. You haven't any ideas that may help, have you?"

Nurse had come round into my line of vision. She was damp and perplexed.

By this time I did have some ideas, but I could not see any method of putting them into practice. Haltingly, I explained that, as far as I could determine, my spitting was caused by the exhalation of air when my body was under pressure in the lung. With an outrush of air, everything else rushed out in its wake; speech; orange juice; and water. The only way to overcome such forceful ejection was for me to be able to control the fluid as it entered my mouth, so that I swallowed only when I was inhaling. The force with which the lung caused me to suck in my breath was equal to the pressure which made me spit, so I concluded that if I were able to fill my mouth with fluid as I was about to inhale, it must automatically be pulled down my throat at the same time as the air. It took me some time to relate all this to Nurse, but she was quick to understand and required no repeated explanations.

"You poor old thing," she said; "you must be fagged out. If only I'd been in one of these myself to get an idea of the difficulties, things would have been much simpler."

"Heaven . . . forbid," I said. I did not mind being in one, because it was a case of necessity as far as I was concerned, but the thought of this gentle, smiling girl shut up in the lung, just for the sake of helping her patients, was not a happy one.

"The next thing is to think of some means whereby you can control——"

46

"Control what? Whatever have you two been up to now? The place reeks of orange!"

Dr Black had come in. Nurse Farley described all that had happened, while he looked appraisingly at the damage.

"Is spitting a national pastime, Down Under?"

"I wish I . . . had a mouth . . ."

"Full? To spit out, this very moment?" He was laughing.

"Yes."

He was standing by Nurse, at the corner of the lung, and for the first time I realized what a tall, strongly-built girl she was. She topped Dr Black, who, at that moment, was drumming his fingers on the top of my box.

"You know, nurse, I think the answer might be a tube—a glass tube, so that you can see what is happening. She ought to be able to control that with her tongue and lips. I'll get one from the dispensary, right away."

He went quickly. The hubbub occasioned by this swallowing performance had turned my thoughts in other directions. "Nurse?"

"Yes?"

"What about . . . other things?"

"What things?"

I racked my brains for appropriate words in which to express myself, but could think of none.

"What goes in . . . must come out."

"Oh, I get you. You are to cease worrying about that. Your other bodily functions are taken care of. You can only cope with one thing at a time, and the most important at the moment is that you should be able to take things into your body. I'll fix what comes out."

"How?"

She opened her eyes. "Do you really want to know?"

"No . . . I mean, how . . . do you get . . . in to me?"

"Oh, I never thought. You can't know, of course. But in either side of the lung there are two round windows—like portholes. They are tightly latched, to prevent any escape of air, and consequent decrease in pressure. These windows, or portholes, are of sufficient size to admit the width of an arm,

47

so when I have to attend to you I open them quickly and thrust my arm in—right up to the shoulder . . . then I can do what needs to be done, while my arm stops any air from coming out. I'll show you." For a moment she stood a little down from the left-hand corner of the lung, then leant quickly across the top of it, and I could feel her fingers grasping mine. I was not alone in that box any more. She turned and smiled. "Simple, isn't it?"

"Yes, but . . . how do you know . . . what you're——"

"What I'm doing?"

"Yes."

She straightened up, withdrew those friendly fingers, and I heard something snap shut. She rapped on the wood above me.

"You hear that? That's wood. The lung is made primarily of wood, but in the top, just above your chest, is an immovable glass window. It's just here." Her rapping made a different noise. "That enables me to see what I'm doing when my hand's inside, and to watch your respiration whenever I want to."

"Do you mind?"

"Mind what? Nursing you?"

"Yes."

"No, I love it. It's my job. Actually, I was awfully pleased when they asked me to special a lung case." There was a smile in her eyes. "I was a bit scared, too. Now you rest while we wait for Doctor Black, and I'll start making out my report. It will take ages to do, because so much has happened today."

I certainly had a gem of a nurse.

My patch of blue was a deep mist of indigo before Dr Black returned. He was not unaccompanied, for, above the noise of the lung and my breathing, I heard the slow trundle of wheels which meant that some heavy object was being moved about the room.

"That'll do, chaps, thanks." Dr Black's voice came from behind my head. "Is there another plug in the room, nurse?"

"Yes, doctor, over here, in this corner."

"Blast—the flex isn't long enough. I'll have to get another. I'll be back in a minute, nurse."

48

Nurse Farley came to me. "I suppose you want to know what goes on?"

"Please."

"I don't, honestly, know myself. He's wheeled in an extraordinary looking contraption. It's standing on a trolley at present. It's got a rubber tube dangling from it."

"To swallow?"

"No, it can't be for that, because he has also brought a collection of bent glass tubes and I guess they're for swallowing purposes. . . . However, we'll find out in time. Not worried, are you?"

"No."

Dr Black presented a masked and perspiring face to me when he returned.

"I have never done so much running around after one woman in my life before." He was puffing. "June, I'm sorry, but you can't tackle any more swallowing today."

"Why not?" Nurse Farley voiced my thoughts.

Dr Black looked over my head. "I ran into Basil Hume on my way to the dispensary. I told him about the tubes and the swallowing, and he's all for it, but—but, I think I'd better leave all this till the morning."

"If it's something she's got to know, now is as good a time as any."

"Mm—well, I've started now, so I may as well carry on." His eyes came back to me. "Hume thinks you'll be able to manage with practice, but he pointed out something I hadn't thought of. You see, if you're swallowing air at the same time as you're swallowing fluid, it is quite possible that things will get a bit complicated and you'll find the fluid in your windpipe. That means, you'll choke—hence, the electric sucker." He indicated the corner where, I gathered, the "extraordinary contraption" was standing. "It's just in case of emergency. If you should run into trouble, we can draw any fluid from your windpipe with that."

"I won't stop . . . breathing?"

"No, we'll take mighty fine care you don't."

"Can't I please . . . try now?"

"No, leave it until morning, when you are rested."

"Doctor Timms——"

"Oh! So that's why you are so keen? You want to put on a show for Duggy Timms?"

"Yes."

"Sorry, the answer is still, 'no'. But I'll tell you what I'll do. I shall be up here, early, and we'll have the thing well in hand before Doctor Timms arrives. Would eight-thirty suit you, nurse?"

"Yes, Doctor Black."

"Good. And, June, you won't worry, will you?"

"No, I've given . . . that up."

"Good for you."

Chapter 5

I HEAR A VOICE

~~~~~~~~VOV~~~~~~~~

The light had been switched on for some time, and Nurse Farley was at my nostrils again, when I heard a voice raised in greeting.

"Hallo, Joyce. You're late, aren't you? How are things?"

"Hallo, Penny. Come round here for a minute." A head appeared above Nurse Farley's bent back.

"Hallo," I said.

Blue eyes opened wide. "The girl speaks!"

Nurse Farley straightened up and I was surprised to see that the second nurse was even taller than she was. "What a day we've had!" Then to me: "This is your night nurse, Penelope Carew." Her grey eyes moved out of sight. "Come on, Penny, there's a whale of a report to go through."

What I had seen of Nurse Carew's face was beautiful beyond mere prettiness: well-spaced eyes, large and clear, with a depth of pure blue that is rarely seen; black, bat-wing eyebrows; an intelligent shapely brow; and black waving hair. If you've got a mouth and nose in tune with all that, I thought, you must have these young doctors running round in circles. Her skin was smooth, and a rose-tinge coloured her high cheek-bones. I had plenty of time to observe her during the night, because sleep proved elusive.

"My dear, I wish you could get some sleep. Can I do anything to make you more comfortable?"

"My neck burns."

"Yes, I noticed that. It's the friction from that jolly collar, and I don't think we can do anything about it. Not without taking you out of the lung, and we can't do that."

"What's the . . . collar like?"

"It's a big, steel affair that fits round your neck."

"What's my head . . ."

"Resting on?"

"Yes."

"Well, in this steel collar are two shafts that stick out about eighteen inches from it. A piece of canvas is stretched across them, and your head is on that."

"Who invented . . ."

"The lung?" These young people were adept at finishing my sentences for me.

"Yes."

"I'm ashamed to say that I don't know. Try and rest, will you? Even if you can't sleep."

It required no effort on my part to lie absolutely still, so, if resting meant lying still, I was at rest all the time. Throughout the night I tried to imagine what it would be like to manipulate a glass tube into suitable positions for interrupted swallowing. I decided that it would be best to hold it in one corner of my mouth with my lips, so that I could make full use of my tongue as a stopper. I was looking forward to the new day.

"Sorry, June, I'll have to wake you. Doctor Black's arrived."

I looked up into grey eyes. "Nurse Carew?"

"She's just gone off duty. She didn't even wake you to wash you, but sleep is more important for you, and we've got all day to wash in."

"All set, nurse?"

"Yes, doctor. Shall I stand behind her? Then you can come here."

"Yes, thanks." Dr Black replaced Nurse Farley.

"Good morning, June. Ready for the fray?"

"Oh, yes . . . put the tube . . . in the corner of . . . my mouth."

I felt something cold in the side of my mouth. I jabbed my tongue at a round opening, waited for an inhalation, released my tongue; then sucked. A cold trickle inside me, but no spitting.

"She's taken some."

"Jolly good show! Take some more, June, but take it easy."

I spluttered a few times in the next ten minutes, and choked, twice, but there was more water inside me than on the lung or Dr Black's white coat. I discovered that my teeth held the tube more securely than my lips, and if I confined everything connected with swallowing to the left side of my mouth, the right was free to allow air to rush wither it would.

"Give her a rest, nurse." He rubbed his hands together. "That's jolly good. . . . Now we can get something with a bit of body into her. Try some orange juice in about half an hour. Get another nurse to hold the tumbler, while you take charge of the sucker."

"Shan't need it," I said.

Dr Black laughed. "I don't think you will, for very long, but we're taking no risks at the moment. I must hurry."

Nurse Farley managed to produce two rather scared-looking juniors, who forgot their fears once they realized that the situation was one demanding only cleanliness and speed. Nurse Farley was astonishing. Usually a soft-spoken, gentle girl, moving unhurriedly, she was transformed into a speed fiend, rapping out orders as her arms dived in and out of the portholes as if she possessed six instead of two. One borrowed nurse did what she could with my nostrils, while the other rubbed a sweet, sticky substance over my teeth, gums, and tongue. Nurse Farley looked down at me.

"Thank goodness your finger-nails can't get dirty inside there." She scrutinized my face, ears, nose, and mouth; then peered into the lung. "You will pass." Basins, face-cloth, towels, a pile of débris that had been thrown onto the top of the lung as it was pulled through the portholes, disappeared with the two extra nurses. All was quiet, except for the hiss of the lung, and the sizzle of my breath.

"Nurse, is there time . . . for orange juice?"

"Yes, of course. The panic's over now."

"Put the tumbler . . . on a chair."

"Why?"

"No need then . . ."

"For another nurse?"

"Yes."

"Well, I don't see why that shouldn't work. I'll still be free to control the sucker."

It was not only a most successful venture, but also a most enjoyable one. Not since I had first been ill had I swallowed anything that was pleasant in my mouth and secure in my stomach. I ran a furtive tongue over my lips. "More, please."

"Not now, sorry. I don't know what I'd do if you started to vomit."

"Use the sucker."

Nurse laughed. "I suppose that would be the answer, but we shall not——" She looked up quickly.

"Good morning, nurse. This my mask?" A brisk competent voice.

"Good morning, Doctor Timms. Yes, I'll tie it for you."

"Well, June! I am told that you have been up to all sorts of tricks."

"Can't see you."

"Oh, sorry. Where shall I stand, nurse?"

"At the top left-hand corner of the lung, sir." Fair hair going grey and brushed well back, spectacles framing keen eyes.

"I've been dying . . . to see you."

There was a laugh, which I recognized as Dr Black's, from nearby. "I told you, sir, you've made quite a hit."

"I think June means that it is nice to be able to see anything."

"I don't."

Dr Timms put back his head and laughed—really laughed—for the first time in my presence. "I want to hear you talk. Tell me what you can do."

Killing several birds with one stone, I thought. "I can see . . . to my left . . . hear normally . . . and feel——"

"Are you sure that you can feel?"

"Pretty sure."

"Right. I'll test you in a moment. Go on."

"I can speak . . . as I breathe out . . . and swallow . . . as I breathe in——"

"There'll be no fear of her talking and eating at the same time, sir, as long as she's in the lung."

I wanted to join in the laughter that followed Dr Black's remark. "I can't laugh."

Dr Timms recovered himself. "Don't worry about that as long as you can enjoy the joke."

"But how do you . . . know that I'm . . . enjoying it?"

"That is something I hadn't thought of. We shall have to take it for granted. And now, I must examine you. I'm afraid that will not be much of a joke. Just say, 'yes', when you feel anything."

He pricked and scraped a pin from toe to neck over the flesh inside the lung. I assuredly could feel: a 'yes-man' had nothing on me. When he had finished with the pin, he waved his finger about in front of me asking me to tell him when it disappeared, he shone a little bright light in my eyes, peered down my throat, and poked around inside my ears. I waited.

"We'll have to do something about that neck, Black. It will be raw if we don't."

Nothing more. After all that pin-pricking the only thing he could talk about was my neck. Practical, kindly, but judiciously non-committal.

"Yes, sir. Nurse is quite worried about it; but what can we do?"

"Strap it well, with adhesive. The widest you can find, but get it on before any skin breaks."

"But that means taking her out of the lung?"

"Yes. Yes. Apply artificial respiration, while you've got her out."

"Yes, sir."

"June, you are doing splendidly. Keep it up. I shall be back tomorrow. Good-bye."

"Thank you . . . good-bye."

Evidently it was mine not to reason why.

Even with someone pushing heavily on my diaphragm to keep breath in my body, it was frightening out of the lung; and fear brought a return of all the horror of previous asphyxiation. I was unaware of anything except the need to get back inside my mechanized life-giver.

After I was safely and happily boxed once more, Dr Black

looked down at me. "Well, June, I don't know about you, but I feel I can breathe again." He was peering through the glass window.

"So do I. . . . Doctor Black?"

"Yes?"

"Who invented . . ."

"The lung?"

"Yes."

"Actually, the man who designed the first lung that was applied practicably and satisfactorily was a fellow called John Drinker. Sometimes they differ in construction, but the principle is the same. This one was donated to St Mary's by Lord Nuffield."

Nurse Farley called Dr Black away and I was left alone with my thoughts, which were centred on Drinker and Nuffield, two more people who had joined the ranks of those to whom I owed a debt I could never hope to repay. My sentiments regarding the lung were no longer ones of loathing and horror, but of inexpressible gratitude for the chance to go on living. I had no wish for life to cease just as it was beginning to shape itself to some purpose. My first impression of the "box" had been that of a coffin on wheels: I remembered the analogy with irony, because I now realized that the lung was the only stop-gap between me and a coffin.

Dr Black's face loomed above me. "Try and rest, June. Give her as much to drink as she wants. I'll be back later, to see how everything is going."

Apart from the contentment induced by a well-filled, if somewhat water-logged, stomach it was a joy to be able to drink. I drank the juice of one orange after another, then pints of water, until I became worried on Nurse Farley's behalf. "Aren't you sick . . . of this drinking?"

"Of course not." I never knew her to admit that anything was a trial to her. "One good thing—it will pacify the path lab."

"Path lab?"

"The pathological laboratory. They've been complaining about the measly specimens I've been sending them."

"Nurse, what is . . . wrong with me?"

Those grey eyes were direct. "They really don't know. They can't seem to decide what it is."

"Do they think . . . I'm infectious?"

"No. I'm pretty sure of that."

"Then why does . . . everyone have a . . ."

"Mask?"

"Yes."

"That's for safety. Yours. So you won't catch any germs that people may be carrying. That's what you are having penicillin injections for, too."

"Oh, thanks."

"And by the way, speaking of the path lab, one of the doctors from there is interested in you and wants to come and read to you some time. Would you like that?"

"Oh, yes please . . . very much. . . . How does he . . . know me?"

Nurse chuckled. "He comes every day to collect specimens and take a blood test. And now you must rest, because your nice Mr Johns will be here this afternoon, and Doctor Timms has told me that he can come when he likes and entertain you as he likes." She pinched my cheek. "Within reason, of course."

Peter came that afternoon, bringing my mail which he read to me, some tulips which Nurse put in a vase for me, and his old cheerful banter which was an antidote against any ills. I good-humouredly abused the lung, because so often a retort sprang to my lips but always I had to consider whether I was inhaling or exhaling, and by that time my remarks were often completely irrelevant to the conversation.

"Nurse, do you think I could bring a book, tomorrow, and read to her?"

"You may do anything you wish."

Nurse, I thought, you're in deep water here, but Peter was content to raise astonished eyebrows before dropping his eyelid over one wicked blue eye.

"What about . . . the other chap?"

"Well, I'll be dashed! I thought I was the only man in your life, Swan. Who, may I ask, is 'the other chap'?"

"Please explain . . . to him, Nurse."

"No, my girl, you'll do your own explaining."

But Nurse came to my rescue and recounted the story of the doctor in the path lab.

Peter, being Peter, shouted with laughter. "That," he said, "beats everything. You stop at nothing. Here you are, boxed in up to the neck, and you get matey over specimens. . . . But seriously, we both ought to be able to fit in one reading a day, don't you think, nurse?"

"Yes, Doctor Timms is all for it."

"Good. I'll say this time in the afternoon. I'll ring and find out if it fits in."

"Oh, you needn't do that. Doctor Meiklejohn works here all day, so he can juggle his times better than you."

"All right, nurse. Keep an eye on this woman. Good-bye, Swan."

Dr Meiklejohn came in that evening as Nurse Farley was going off duty. He was a fair, square young man, clad in a white coat punctured with acid holes. Nurse Carew came and stood beside him while he enquired after my welfare. I wondered how he could turn his attention to anything except the loveliness so near at hand. Suddenly, he did turn to it. "Penny, what about coming to the Students' Ball with me?" I silently wished him luck.

"Sorry, Mike, I'm going with Bob Worthington."

"Oh, nurse!" I said.

Blue eyes, shot with violet, opened wide in astonishment. "What a tone of reproach!" She turned to Dr Meiklejohn. "It seems our patient is keen to choose my escort for me, but I've promised Bob, so that's all there is about it. Now, you go to sleep and stop deciding who is taking me where."

During the days and nights that followed, both my nurses were wonderful. They spoke encouragement and comfort even when they were unable to do anything to relieve pain. Never once was there a word of censure for me, and their patience and attentiveness stopped many a word of complaint on my lips. Dr Meiklejohn and Peter relieved the tedium of the day by reading. I tried to tell them something of my appreciation, because they never once failed me. Apart from the printed pages they spilled into my ears, their daily appearances did much to restore equanimity to my frequently troubled mind. No human being could lie in a box, day and night, without wondering what it was all about and where it was going to end. Sleep came desultorily, leaving too many waking hours in which to ponder on the unpredictability of my position.

Visitors came and went, but they were always masked, so I had no clear idea of their identity. Names were spoken which conveyed little, except that they were related to the Smiths who lived across the river from us at home, or were second cousins of someone with whom I had been to college. The New Zealand High Commissioner was becoming well known and beloved by the hospital staff. He knew nothing about me except that I was a fellow countryman, but I had been told his first comment on seeing me: "Nothing must be spared her," he had said. And nothing was. When he became aware that my consumption of orange juice was causing an orange crisis in the hospital he took the situation into his capable, kindly hands and had cases of them sent to my little room.

My visitors, with the exception of Peter, stayed only a minute or two. Mostly, I think, the sight of me horrified them, but they came bravely, and spoke cheerfully. My friends at home wrote not only to me, but to anyone in England with whom they had any link at all. It is not difficult for people in a distant country to write asking friends, or relations, to visit someone in an iron lung in a London hospital. Those people who wrote knew me and were concerned about me: those to whom they wrote knew me not and consequently could not be expected to be concerned on my behalf. It was not a pleasant task, but they came, and their coming renewed my oft-times flagging determination to get out of the hole I was in.

A pretty, dark sister, who looked like a ballet dancer, was always at hand to assist Nurse Farley, and one day, as she pulled her arm out of the porthole and straightened up, she turned dark questioning eyes on me.

"What about something to eat, June?"

"Eat? . . . I'd never thought . . . about that."

"I know you hadn't. But you have got to start. You can't live on orange juice and glucose for the rest of your life. Besides, you want to get strong again, don't you?"

"Certainly."

"Well now—if you were perfectly free to choose, what would you fancy most?"

I had to think that one over. She waited.

"Sardines," I said.

She laughed aloud. "Very well, I'll see what I can do." She was back in half an hour carrying a saucer, in which were six tiny cubes of thin bread and butter well covered with sieved sardine. She popped one inside my mouth.

"Mm," I said.

I ate them all. After that I was spoilt; woefully spoilt. There was not much that I cared to eat, but whatever it was, it was produced from somewhere at any time of the night or day. Penny scrambled an egg for me in the middle of the night, and when I apologized, because I could only manage four spoonfuls of it, she patted me on the cheek in pleased acknowledgement of what I had consumed, and said not one word of disapprobation about what was left on the plate.

Dr Black came every day; Dr Timms twice, or three times, a week; and every night, at the same time, a man came in with a torch. All I ever saw of him was a beam of light.

"Nurse Carew?"

"Yes?"

"Who is the man . . . that comes in . . . every night——"

"With a torch?"

"Yes."

"He is the head engineer in the hospital. He comes in to check the lung, and see that everything is in working order."

"What a confoun . . . ded nuisance I . . ."

"June, for heaven's sake, stop that!" Nurse Carew's voice was sharp. "Sorry I snapped, my dear—and by the way, it's about time you dropped this Nurse Carew business and called me Penny, except, of course, when matron's about—but you mustn't get ideas that you are a nuisance. We're brought up in

60

a pretty tough school, and we'd soon tell you if you were. In future, you let us decide."

"Sorry, nurse."

"Penny."

"All right . . . Penny."

"Good. And now, to see if you have really got over your lapse, I'll tell you something about the engineer that I think you ought to know. . . . The day they put you into the lung, Mr Taylor—that's the engineer—was due for three weeks' holiday. He had planned to take his wife and two children to Brighton. When he was called in to set up the lung, he didn't cancel his holiday, but he cancelled his reservations, and took his holiday in his home—which is not far from here—so that he could come up to hospital every night, check the mechanism of the lung, and be on the spot if anything went wrong with it."

"He wasn't . . . asked?"

"No, he wasn't. But he realized that while you're in the lung, your life is in the hands of a mechanic, as much as a doctor. He offered to stay."

"Could I . . . thank him?"

She hesitated. "Actually, I think he'd be most embarrassed if you spoke to him, as things are at the moment. Wait until you're better."

"When will I . . . be better?"

"I don't know. No one knows. But you will be, never fear."

"Thanks for telling . . . me about . . ."

"Mr Taylor?"

"Yes. Is there . . . anyone else?"

"You mean, like Mr Taylor? That you should know about?"

"Yes."

"No. You don't strike many people like him very often."

Penny had a flair for keeping my mind away from my own troubles, and during the night she often recounted scraps of interest from the life of the hospital which familiarized me with its organization. It was a teaching hospital, carrying several hundred medical students, who were lectured to, and trained by, a staff of top-flight surgeons, physicians, gynaecologists, neurologists, and the like. There was the nursing staff, people called almoners, others called physiotherapists both trained and in training, dietitians, the domestic staff, porters, and orderlies. In charge of the administration of the entire hospital was a man whom she called a House Governor. He was a colonel, not a medical man, and I did not envy him his task.

My days passed more quickly than my nights because there was a constant routine of activity which commanded my attention. Nurse Farley washed me in easy stages: I sipped at orange drink; I had my readers and the visits of the doctors.

One afternoon, shortly after Peter had left, a man's face appeared above the corner of the lung. There was no time to recollect whose it was, because a hand was raised in salute, and a plummy English voice said: "Gregory Richardson Alverton-Young at your service."

"Gray! . . . what brings you . . . here?"

"You, of course."

"But how did you . . . know?"

"Well, that is quite a long story, really. My mother belongs to a bridge circle in London, and one of its members received food parcels from someone in New Zealand during the war. They have continued corresponding, and apparently you lived, or boarded or something, with this person—anyway, she wrote and asked mother's friend if she could find out anything about you. She—this friend—was discussing it over the bridge table and mother connected smartly because I'd told her all about meeting you. And here I am." He paused and drew breath. "Sorry we didn't know before. All the others at the Royal College who met you want to come and see you, if they're allowed. I was sent as an envoy, as it were. My mother sends her good wishes."

We talked until Nurse Farley tapped him on the shoulder. "It's time to go."

"Oh, very well. Look, June, may I write to your mother?"

"Thanks," I said, thinking that as far as news was concerned the more mother had of me the better. "Tell her I look . . . all right, please."

"Yes, I'll exert myself and pen a most glowing account."

He took my home address. "By the way—what's your nurse's name?"

"Joyce Farley. . . . She's grand."

"I've no doubt about that. Cheerio."

His visits became part of the daily round, and we gave up attempting to convince people that we were not brother and sister or that, in fact, no blood relationship existed between us. He was never permitted more than a few minutes with me, so I wondered at the frequency of his visits, until one day I noticed that, although he spoke to me, his eyes constantly wandered over the top of my head where all eyes were turned when Nurse was being addressed. That he had glimpsed some lovely part of her character from those grey, smiling eyes was obvious, and strengthened the bond that our extraordinary physical resemblance had already established between us. If he—as a man—felt towards Nurse Farley as I did, he would want to visit her patient more than once a day. As for Nurse, she was not one to talk about herself at all, and I could not decide whether she guessed, or how she felt, but, like most females of the species, I did what I could to foster a reciprocal appreciation, without actually throwing Gray at her.

It was an air letter from my mother, fourteen thousand miles distant, that provided some indication of her feelings She was reading it to me in her customary restful tones, when she stopped abruptly, and continued to read in silence. A vivid blush overtopped her mask.

"What's the matter?"

She looked most confused. "Oh, it's Gray. Your mother's had a letter from him."

"Well, he said he'd . . . write. Please go . . . on."

"Yes, I must, but—but . . . I wonder what he said to her?"

"Oh, nurse, please!"

"Sorry." She gave an embarrassed laugh. "The letter continues, 'I had a long, and most enlightening letter from a young man who signs himself Gray. It is the first time anyone has ever told me about your nurse. I was quite amused because two-thirds of his letter was about her. She sounds really lovely.'"

"Oh, nurse!" The cat was properly out of the bag. Mother, I supposed, thought that Peter read all my mail to me.

"Isn't it dreadful. Your poor mother."

"No, nurse, no . . . really, she'd love . . . to hear things like . . . that."

When Gray came that day I told him that he had better explain to Nurse Farley just what he had put in that letter to my mother. He ran his hand over his head.

"It was the truth, anyway."

"Tell her so."

Nurse could not escape because she had to stay near me. They talked for some time until Gray's fair head came into view again.

"Your mother has done me quite a service," he said.

"I'm so glad."

He was gone, and Nurse Farley came, all sobriety and efficiency, to give me an injection.

"Nurse?"

"I'm not going to look at you, June, because all I'll get will be an outrageous and wicked wink." Then I heard her gay chuckle. "You're as bad as he is." She looked down at last. "Very well, I'm going to a show with him on Thursday."

It was sweltering inside the box, but I had to be kept warm; it was apparently part of my cure. I looked up at my patch of blue. It showed me a lovely day, and I wondered what cowslips looked like: I had never ever seen one—but they must have finished blooming by now.

"What are you thinking about?" A deep, clear voice from a tall broad figure in blue. No funny bonnet on her head, but a flowing white veil framing a strong face.

"England in the . . . springtime."

"Are you, my dear? It really is lovely. There is nothing like an English spring. Nurse?"

"Yes, Matron?"

"I have some books, with coloured plates of spring flowers, in my room. I shall send them up, and you can show them to June." She turned to me. "We'll try and bring some springtime into your room, even if it is a little late."

64

"Thank you." She had gone noiselessly. "Nurse?"

"Yes?"

"Matron doesn't . . . know how springy . . . we are in here."

From the sudden flood of colour in Nurse Farley's face I suspected she was thinking along the same lines as I was.

"Really, you're the end! Are they all like you in New Zealand?"

"Worse."

"They couldn't be. Now, would you like an iced orange drink?"

It was lovely, but like all cool things on hot days it soon made me feel hotter than ever. I wondered how much longer I should have to pump out my existence in an iron lung. I continued to wonder until the day I awoke from one of my spasmodic sleeps to hear voices from where I knew the doorway of my room to be. A rich bass voice, inclined to abruptness, was barking unmistakable indignation:

"Great Scott, man! I can't do anything with her in that thing. If she can get herself out of it, let me know."

That was all I heard, but it was sufficient. My head was joined to a dead body, but that was no excuse for my brain to rot. Mentally I kicked myself, because the idea that the struggle to get myself out of the lung was my struggle had never crossed my mind. I fondly imagined that, one fine day, I should automatically be able to do without it. I spared a grateful thought to the man whose few words were my spur and turned my attention to the battle.

"Miss Farley?"

"Yes, Miss Opie."

"Did you hear . . . that?"

"What? Mr Muir talking to Doctor Timms?"

I did not care who had been talking to whom. "That bit about . . . getting myself——"

"Out of the lung?"

"I want to make . . . a start."

"Phew! When you get an idea, you certainly don't let any grass grow under your feet. I'll see Doctor Black."

"Now?"

"Yes, Miss Impatience. Right now."

Both Dr Black and Dr Timms arrived in answer to Nurse's 'phone call. I was to be taken out of the lung for short intervals, gradually increasing the time between coming out and going back.

"How long will it . . . take?"

Dr Timms answered me. "We don't know. But when you can stay out of the lung for an hour, without a break, and without collapsing, we'll take up the reins and transfer you to something else."

"May I start . . . right away?"

"Yes. You stay, Black. I must get back to that lecture. Ring me. I'll be in Victoria ward."

"Do we just switch the lung off for a few seconds, sir?"

"No, no. Not on any account. Never turn the lung off. Take her out. That clear, Nurse?"

"Yes, sir."

"Good luck, June." He vanished.

"I'll wheel her out, nurse. You watch for signs of cyanosing."

Dr Black unscrewed, then unclasped, two big steel clips on either side of the lung, just above my dog collar. I was taken completely by surprise as I found the bottom of the box, on which I was lying, and the top end, through which my head poked like someone in stocks, separated from the remaining four sides. They were left standing, on long steel legs, while I was wheeled from under them with my dog collar still firmly attached to me. The noise of the lung continued, but there was no air-tight compartment now to enclose the hiss from the bellows.

My most obstinate deterrent was fear: fear that I could not go on breathing without mechanical assistance. Anyone who is frightened instinctively catches his breath, and, when there is little or no breath to catch, anything is likely to happen. That first effort was rather calamitous.

Safely boxed again, I decided that it was very easy to get into the lung: all that was required was that one should stop breathing. It was not going to be easy to get out.

66

During the night I lectured myself severely. It was obvious to me that I had become addicted to the lung, and the process of weaning myself away from it was going to be a race against time. I knew that I could not dismiss fear, but I determined to do my utmost to check it in order to draw what breath I could.

Next day we began a new campaign by opening first one porthole, then the other, and with the consequent diminution in pressure I was forced to control my breathing to a certain extent. It was a beginning, and from that I gradually began to forge ahead, perhaps a minute one day; the next, two. When I had done with portholes, I started coming out of the lung, plus dog collar and the bottom side of the box, for short intervals. Those intervals were extremely short for some time. Nurse Farley had to enlist extra help, and it was a difficult task for the nurses, as they had to keep a constant check on my pulse and my breathing; watch for the first signs of asphyxiation; and be ready to wheel me back into the lung on the instant. It seemed as if I was never going to overcome the fear that accompanied this business of being forced to breathe without assistance. I was terrified, and this did not lighten the burden of the nurses. There were no set periods for our experiments, but we found that they were usually more successful immediately I awoke from one of my spasmodic sleeps. If it was two o'clock in the morning when I felt capable of a "breather"—or "gasper", as the nurses called it—I was never refused. Penny collected two or three nurses from somewhere, and out I came. I was not getting myself out of the lung at all. My bid for freedom would have been in vain without the patience and reassurance of the nurses.

During this time my right eye began to focus with more certainty, so I asked Dr Black if there was any possibility of arrangements being made for me to do my own reading. He jumped at the suggestion, and put the matter into the hands of the head engineer, who soon appeared, with a kit of tools, a sheet of glass, and a warrior-like gleam in his eye. Whether he liked it or not, I was determined to waste no more time before thanking him for his nightly visits. He heard me out, but was so occupied nailing things to my box that he showed only the slightest trace of embarrassment. I was very glad that he was not hammering nails into my coffin.

When Mr Taylor left, there was a sheet of plate glass, about eighteen inches square, protruding from the top of the lung directly over my face. Nurse placed an open book, face downwards, on it. I could read. But I could not turn over the pages. "Nurse, you'll have . . ."

"To turn over the pages for you? I realize that."

I learnt to memorize the last sentence, or parts thereof, at the bottom of the right-hand page of my reading, because Nurse Farley was sometimes unable to drop what she was doing and turn the page immediately I asked.

The battle against the lung was waged unceasingly. After I had reached a fifteen-minute breathing space we seemed to come to a standstill: I could not improve upon the time. I was able to stay out more often, but not for greater periods. This eventually passed, and my times began to increase once more. On a Friday morning, from half-past nine to half-past ten, I spent my first full hour out of the lung. Nurse Farley waited only to wheel me back before summoning Dr Black.

He rubbed his hands delightedly. "Splendid! Don't take her out any more, nurse, until I get hold of Duggy Timms."

It was not long before the heavy tramping of feet heralded the arrival of many more people than just Dr Timms and Dr Black. Something was pushed clumsily and noisily into the room.

"That's your bed," whispered Nurse Farley.

A bed, a proper bed, with a mattress: something wide and soft to lie on and a pillow for my head—it sounded like a little spot in Heaven. I was trying very hard not to get excited, because I knew that I must save every ounce of brawn and brain to concentrate on breathing by myself, when they asked it of me.

Dr Timms was at the corner of the lung.

"June, we are going to put you into a respirator that straps round your body, and then transfer you to a bed. Don't think of anything, except your breathing. Take no notice of us. It will feel very strange, and a little frightening at first, but try

68

to forget everything except breathing. We are all here, and we shall not let anything happen to you. Bed ready, Sister?"

"Yes, Doctor Timms."

"Black?"

"Yes, sir." I heard a sudden noise like the suction cups of a milking machine.

"Now, June, we're going to start. Take her out, please, nurse."

The lung was switched off. I puffed frantically, in and out, because my life depended on it: then I realized that a great weight had been lifted from my neck. I was free of my steel collar; and freedom from that was so blessed that I puffed with renewed vigour for fear of finding myself in its clutches once more. Hands were lifting my body. I was lowered onto something cold and rough, which was pulled tighter and tighter around me until I could not puff any more. And that is where fear stepped in.

"Three on either side, and lift her over to the bed."

But I did not care about beds now. There was only one safe place that I knew and that was where I wanted to be: in the lung. Terror made me desperate.

"Put me back."

"You will be all right, June. Think about your breathing."

That was just what I was thinking about, and I was never more convinced of anything in my life, than I was that there was only one place for me to breathe: and that was in the box.

"I hate this."

"Take it steadily. You will be all right."

"Please put me back." I behaved shockingly: then excitement, fear, and disappointment, but mostly fear, made me vomit.

"She's fighting it, sir."

Dr Timms bent over me and said beseechingly: "June, please try and breathe with the respirator. When it closes tightly on you, breathe out, and when it loosens, breathe in."

"It's too slow." Exhaustion made my voice a whisper.

"I miss . . . the noise."

It was an idiotic thing to say, but true. I missed that steady rhythmical hiss of the lung. It meant breath to me.

"Turn the lung on, Black, and we shall adjust the movement of the respirator to the sound of the lung."

That saved me from humiliation and defeat. It also, when I came to reflect upon it in my saner moments, showed me how gutless I could be. If I could manage with noise, which was purely extraneous, then I ought to have managed without noise.

"June, swallow this."

I gulped something bitter. "I'm sorry," I whispered.

"You've been a Briton. Now, go to sleep."

Chapter 6

SPOTS BEFORE MY EYES

━━∽ᴠᴠᴠᴜᴜᴜ(O)ᴜᴜᴜᴜ∽━━

I awoke to a new world. My eyes swept hungrily where they could. There were walls, one with a doorway opening on a corridor, the other two with windows; and there was a polished floor, with a table on it, to the left of me. I never knew a table could look so beautiful. It was a silly little affair, but it was something that was homely, secure, and not at all strange or out of place. So much of my lung life had seemed out of place. There was a screen leaning against the foot of my bed. And my bed . . . it was just an ordinary bed, but I loved it. It seemed immense, and it was covered with a snowy counterpane. Poking out behind the screen was the nose of a long, white box from which a pumping hiss was issuing. Good-bye, my friend, I thought, you were very good to me, but I hope I never have to become as intimate with you again. I pursed my lips and blew a noisy kiss of dismissal. Then I wondered about my speech, for, with my new-found freedom, I ought to be able to talk without interruption.

"Hallo, how are you? I'm fine and dandy, thank you very much, thank you very much, thank you very——"

"June, are you all right?" A quick scurry of feet, and an anxious voice.

"Yes"—I was going to say more, but before me stood the dark, pansy-eyed sister that often assisted Nurse Farley. It was not only her face that resembled a ballet dancer: her neat ankles, dainty figure, and the way she held her head on her shoulders, had all the grace and beauty of one.

"Whatever are you looking at me like that for?" She gave an embarrassed laugh.

"Your figure. You'll have to excuse me, Sister, but I've never seen you full length before."

"Of course you haven't. How nice to hear you saying such a long sentence, all in one. Nurse Farley will be sorry she wasn't here. She ought to be back any minute now. How do you feel?"

"Marvellous, Sister. I'm so happy. I wish I could write and tell my parents."

Then I saw Nurse Farley coming through the doorway. It was the first time I had seen the lower half of her face: she was unmasked. She was out of sight for a few seconds before she appeared at Sister's side, a piece of gauze covering her mouth.

"Hallo! You're awake. How do you feel?"

"I am too busy to feel anything. Please stand over further towards the window, so that I can take you all in."

Sister laughed. "Your turn, now, nurse. She has just finished running over all my finer anatomical points."

The grey eyes smiled. "I see I'm going to have a dreadful time with you, June, now you are able to talk without a break, and with those eyes of yours able to see so much more."

"Nurse, would you write a letter to her parents for her? She's very keen to tell them how she feels."

"Of course, Sister. I'd love to."

"Good-bye, June. Don't overtax yourself."

"Good-bye, Sister."

Nurse brought me a drink. "What on earth?" she said. But I had discovered that I could swallow, without wondering whether I was breathing in or out, and I was not pausing to answer questions. A gurgling noise from the bottom of the glass tube, indicating that I had emptied the tumbler, took us both by surprise. We looked at each other in amazement. She laughed, and I found that my release from the lung had not released any laughter in me, so I winked.

Although my sentences were unbroken, I was still unable to speak for any length of time. Nurse made me rest frequently, so that dictation proceeded slowly. When we had finished, I asked her what the name of the contraption was that was strapped around me.

"It's called a Paul Brag pulsator. Paul Brag being the name of the man who invented it."

"It's great, isn't it?"

"It is recognized as a very valuable piece of equipment when it comes to getting patients out of iron lungs."

It was like a strait-jacket: I glanced up at the white box, and thought that if I had stayed in it much longer I should have been in need of one.

"Nurse, you can turn the lung off. I don't need the noise any more."

"Sure?"

"Yes, quite sure."

There was a sudden silence, then the apologetic chug of the battery controlling my new breathing apparatus made itself heard.

Nurse looked up. "Sounds queer, doesn't it?"

"Yes, but it's a nice kind of queerness."

My new respirator was a two-way rubber jacket, fitting tightly round my body from groin to armpits. To it were attached two pieces of rubber tubing that led to a machine run by a battery. One of these tubes pushed air into the Paul Brag, to inflate it, while the other sucked air from it, to deflate it. The result was that of someone administering artificial respiration with their hands clasped round my ribs, increasing and decreasing the lung space to allow breathing to continue. Its advantages over the lung were many, the most important of which lay in the fact that, while I was in the pulsator, a certain amount of breathing control was required of me.

"All right, June?" Nurse Farley was busy with the body under the bedclothes.

"Yes, thank you."

She looked at me sternly. "Something is wrong with you. I wish you would tell me—it makes things easier."

"I've got a splitting head, Nurse, and I feel sick."

"Oh." She went through a temperature-pulse routine and sent for Dr Black.

He looked at me thoughtfully. "I think it's all a matter of position. Take her pillows away, nurse. . . . Is that better, June?"

"My head still feels too high."

"I'll get some blocks, nurse." He was back in no time carrying two pieces of white wood, shaped like cones, but sawn off at the apex. He put them on the floor. "Could you manage the other side please, nurse?"

"Hang on—I'll give you a lift." A man's voice coming from the doorway. "I'll just cover up with a yashmak first."

Peter took one side of the bed, Dr Black the other, and Nurse slipped the blocks under the legs at the foot.

"You'll feel better now, June."

Nurse Farley was looking at Peter, who was pointing a long finger at me. "You wonder why I call her Swan—just look at the length of that neck!"

Dr Black's laughter died on his lips. "My word, nurse, just look at that neck."

"I know, Doctor Black. The adhesive plaster. I've tried—it's hopeless. It seems to have grown into her flesh."

They tried, by fair means and foul, to remove it; but it was still adhering to me when Dr Timms arrived the following morning accompanied by Dr Black, complete with scribbling block, and several white-coated figures. They all had stethoscopes and from the large, square pockets of their coats protruded an array of professional weapons.

"We'll do her chest first, Hume, before she tires." Dr Timms turned to me. "We shall have to unbuckle the pulsator for a few minutes, June."

That did not worry me because I had become accustomed, while in the lung, to breathe for short intervals without assistance. The cold disc on the end of the green-eyed doctor's stethoscope was poked about my torso. He wasted no time, and it was not long before he straightened up, speaking to Dr Timms in an incomprehensible mumble-jumble of medical jargon. Dr Timms pushed an even colder round of metal on to the spot Dr Hume was indicating; then they buckled me into the jacket without further ado. They turned back the bedclothes at the foot of my bed; drew something sharp up the soles of my feet; bent my legs over their arms and hit my knees with a rubber tyre on the end of a stick; did the same with my arms; and gave me strips of paper which I was supposed to hold between my fingers, but which—try as I would—just slipped through.

It was the first time I had seen my hands, and their lack of flesh appalled me. I wondered what my legs were like: I had been unable to see anything of them as the doctors bent their backs over them to bang my knees. They asked me to lift my head, but it was anchored fast to the mattress; they went through all their finger-waving exercises; then they went to work with a pin again. Finally they stopped; rolled the bed-clothes back onto my cold body; and left, with nothing more than a spoken farewell.

Nurse Farley was pushing a little warm blanket in under the cradle, over my legs.

"Nurse, do they know yet what is wrong with me?"

"No, June, they don't."

"But they must. I've been here for ages, and they must know something after they've just examined me."

"They don't know, honestly. They haven't decided."

Before my illness I had known that there were such things as iron lungs, but they were nothing more than a name to me. I knew I had been unable to breathe without one. But on the cause of my inability to breathe I was wholly ignorant. I grew so tired of wondering that I eventually made my own diagnosis. The doctors could think what they pleased: I had spinal meningitis, from which, I reckoned, it was only a question of time before I should recover completely. This thought kept me very happy.

On the afternoon of the day I had been examined so thoroughly, Dr Black and Nurse Farley, on the advice of Dr Timms, removed the adhesive plaster with ether. It was a ticklish job, and I was grateful to them, because it was comforting to know that I was being kept as wholesome as circumstances permitted.

With the idea that I must be launched into society once more, I was moved into a small ward four days later. It was an experimental penicillin ward containing six patients, including myself. I missed my patch of blue, but Nurse Farley and Penny were to continue "specialling" me, as they called it. This comforted me, because they were both tall, strong girls who could handle my body gently but firmly: also I was very fond of them, and had no wish to see them go.

My first hour in society was spent listening to the personal medical history of the patient in the bed next to me. She was suffering from rheumatoid arthritis, and she did not spare me one detail of the pain she was called upon to bear. She droned on and on. I have no doubt she was "in a bad way" as she put it, but I did wish she would cease talking about it. Nurse Farley came back from lunch and cut short the drone by placing screens round my bed.

"How long has that been going on?" She nodded towards the next bed.

"Ever since you left."

"You poor kid. We'll see that you don't have to listen to any more of that."

"Nurse, you've forgotten to put your mask on. Not that I don't like seeing your whole face."

She had a softly curling mouth which widened into a lovely smile. "We don't have to wear them any more."

"Good. You look much nicer without one."

"That's just what——" She went crimson and clapped her hand over her mouth.

"Go on, please." Then her blush gave me the clue to her unfinished sentence. "Is that what Gray said, when he saw you without one?"

She pinched my cheek. "Well, yes, it was him, but you needn't spread it about."

"No, Nurse—it's only that I'm so pleased."

"You're a funny old thing . . . and now I have got to tidy up all your charts, so you must rest. I'll be here, but I don't want you to talk, unless you want me."

I was lying perfectly flat in my bed, which was still blocked at the foot end; I had no pillow, and I was staring at a cream-glazed ceiling. To my consternation I suddenly found that pink spots were appearing in front of my eyes. Every now and then a peculiar pink haze appeared to blot out my vision. I lay there, in a fever of anticipation, waiting for the next blur to appear. They were consistent; coming at regular intervals, seeming to hover for a few seconds before disappearing, only to return later. This continued, until I was nearly driven frantic, so I decided that, charts or no charts, I must disturb Nurse. When I told her, she took one quick look at me.

"Will you be all right while I phone Doctor Black?"

"Of course."

When he came he looked at me anxiously. "Tell me about these pink spots, June."

I gave him a graphic description of what was happening. He took my pulse, my temperature, waved his finger backwards and forwards before my eyes, then peered into them with a little bright light. He looked relieved, but extremely puzzled. "Any pain?"

"No, doctor."

"Are you sure you can see those pink spots?"

"Yes——" Then I cried: "There's one now. It always happens when I look directly at the ceiling."

He was standing on the left-hand side of my bed, close to my head, and I suppose he must have instinctively tilted his head to look in the same direction.

Suddenly he cried, in a tone of complete bewilderment: "By Jove! I can see them too . . . or am I mad?"

Nurse Farley was directed to stand on the other side of the bed, with her head tilted backwards. The three of us gazed fixedly at the ceiling. It was not long before Nurse also began to see them. We could not be mad, all three of us, but we could see those pink spots.

Suddenly Nurse brought her head forward. "Listen!" she said. I could hear nothing, but both she and Dr Black rushed to the window behind my bed. The mystery was solved. There was a bus stop on a street, directly below my window. As it was a bright sunny day, the red-painted London omnibuses were throwing a faint pink reflection through the window and on the ceiling of the ward. The regularity with which the spots continued to appear and disappear coincided with the arrival and departure of the omnibuses.

"I'm terribly sorry, Doctor Black."

"You are probably laughing your head off. Anyway, there is no need for apologies—they had me completely fooled."

Peter had started reading to me again, because there was no way of fixing a glass plate above my head now that I was in an ordinary bed. He was a most accommodating visitor for, apart from his entertainment value, he could give me drinks, and manipulate the pump that was attached to the pulsator machine.

There was quite a variety of diseases in the ward, for St Mary's is the home of penicillin, and this was the ward that was devoted solely to the work concerned with penicillin research. The patients received it in every conceivable shape and form. I discovered penicillin could be manufactured in powder form, as a liquid, as a cream; it could be swallowed, or sucked, inhaled, applied internally, or externally, and injected by means of a hypodermic syringe. Dr Meiklejohn was constantly required in the ward on pathological business, so I saw much more of him than when I had been in the lung.

He crossed quickly over to my bed one morning, holding a stand-full of test-tubes, containing what looked to me like cream wicks suspended in clear fluid. "Can't stop long, June, but how are you?" He was standing between my bed and the machine.

I could not speak, because I had suddenly stopped breathing. My face felt hot, and my eyes seemed to have grown stalks.

"Good heavens! Whatever is the matter? You look as if you're about to become asphyxiated."

I could not answer. My eyes swivelled in the direction of the floor.

He looked down enquiringly—and, with an oath, jumped off the rubber tubing.

"What a damned stupid place to leave those air tubes! I might have killed you!"

To obviate further casualties, Dr Timms had the tubes lifted off the floor and suspended on a wooden frame.

As the days went by my little engine did not chug so constantly. I could eat, sleep, talk, see, hear, smell, and feel—although I was not particularly happy about some of the things I could feel at times. My nurses could leave me alone for part

of the day and help in the ward. On their days off, a relief
came, but only to wash me and attend to my bodily needs: for
the remainder of the day, I was cared for by Sister and her staff.

In the late afternoon of one such day a very young, fair
nurse was sitting by my bed, cutting my fingernails. It was a
fiddlesome business.

"What a pass to come to, nurse."

She glanced at me briefly. "What do you mean?"

"Fancy having to depend on someone else to cut your
fingernails."

She went on cutting. "Oh, well, you've got to accustom
yourself to the thought that you'll have to depend on lots of
things, before you're better."

"Yes, I know. Things like crutches, perhaps?"

"Yes, and irons."

"IRONS!" Cold, horrid fear took hold of me. "Irons! But
nurse, only people with infantile paralysis wear irons."

Confusion burned her face. "Forget it—you won't need
them." Her words meant nothing, but that flush of red meant
guilt; guilt that what she had said had put me on the track of
something I was not supposed to guess.

I said nothing more to her about it; in fact, I said very little
to anybody, about anything, for the remainder of the day.
Sister came to me before going off duty.

"You're very quiet, June. Is anything wrong?"

"No, Sister. I'm fine, thank you."

"Good night, then."

"Good night, Sister."

It was not a very good night. Penny worried, and in the end
I grew so despairing and frightened, lying there turning my
ghastly fears round and round in my head, that I told her.

"Penny, I'd never thought of infantile paralysis before . . ."
It was all I could do to speak the awful words, because I knew
so well what they meant. I also knew that, if that was what I
had, it was not a light attack.

Then Dr Black was by my bed, listening to my fears. He took
my skinny hand in his. I loathed my hand in that instant.

"June," he said, "if I promise you that tomorrow I'll get

79

Doctor Timms to come and clear all this up for you, will you promise me to try and get some sleep?"

"No fooling about, and shelving the question?"

"No. I promise."

"All right. I'll try and sleep."

Chapter 7

THE TRUTH AND A BIG MAN

———◦∿∿∿◦◯◦∿∿∿◦———

Next morning Dr Timms came. He was by himself: no white coat, no stethoscope, no paraphernalia, and nobody. He put screens round my bed, sat down on a chair by my side, and took my hand in his.

"June, we are sure, now, that you are not going to die; but this is going to take a very long time."

He could not have chosen better words as a prelude to what he had to tell me. Even as I was, I preferred life to death. I was not afraid to die, but I was too young not to want to be alive. He told me that I had infantile paralysis. He told me a great many other things too, because he was courteous, as well as kind, and was not going to leave his patient until things had assumed more or less normal proportions.

"June, if you want to cry, go ahead. It is nothing to be ashamed of."

"Have you known for very long, Doctor Timms?"

"Yes, my dear, before you went into the lung. That was one of our private horrors—just to see you lying there, not knowing where the paralysis was going to start or end, and being able to do nothing about it."

"Why didn't you tell me before?"

"You were too ill. I'd have kept it from you longer, if possible, but our luck couldn't hold for ever. An unwitting word had to be dropped, sooner or later."

"Has everyone known?"

"Yes. Your parents know—all your visitors know, but have been warned not to mention the word 'paralysis' to you."

"This has been rather unpleasant for you?"

"What do you mean?"

"I mean, coming here this morning, knowing what you had to tell me." He looked at me without speaking. "Anyway," I went on, "thank you very much. I'll be all right, now."

He removed the screens. "Good-bye," he said: then, without a look or a word for anyone else, he walked, with erect back and purposeful step, straight out of the swinging glass doors of the ward. That was the greatest compliment he could have paid me. Sister's room was at the other end of the ward. He never gave it so much as a glance.

There was no question of dismissing everything with a shrug. It had to be faced, and the sooner I grew accustomed to looking it squarely in the eye the better. I realized that I must never, never, make the mistake of accepting it as irrevocable. I must fight this confounding thing, because I wanted terribly to live, and my idea of life did not include being attached to a dead body for the next fifty years or so. I thought of the beauty of nature that had always surrounded me. The sweeping curve of the ocean breakers; the frosted eddies of foam that curled up the river on a full spring tide; the scud of burnished cloud across an evening sky; the green drift of the delicate foliage of the rimu; the waving tendrils of sea anemones: and how we stood dropping pebbles into rock pools on the reef, for the sheer joy of watching the ripples of clear water, moving ever outwards, until they disappeared. I loved movement that held grace and rhythm: it was life to me. . . .

Sudden hate for my body overwhelmed me: then I wondered if that was the answer. If I fostered hate, would it urge me on like the prick of a spur, or would it kill all endeavour? One thing was certain: I had to come to grips with my paralysed body. I called Nurse Farley.

"Would it be quite in order for you to show me my legs, please?"

She came close to my bed, and said in a very quiet voice: "Do you really want to see them?"

"Yes, please—right now, if it's not against all rules and regulations."

82

She removed bedclothes and cradle, then, holding my right leg behind ankle and knee, she raised it into the air for my inspection.

Its thinness made it appear incredibly long and I was surprised by its smoothness. Shininess would have made it repulsive: it was not shiny, but all the crease marks round my knees and toes had gone. I could not hate that skinny, pitiful limb. It would have to be coaxed, petted, and cared for, if it was to carry me again. Hate was out. I was relieved about that, and out of my relief came a flicker of amused affection for that forlorn leg. I felt a lot happier.

"Thanks very much, nurse. You can put it away now . . . the other one's the same, I suppose?"

"Yes."

"And the rest of me?"

"Yes."

Nurse Farley was off duty when Peter came, in the afternoon, to visit me. He had been reading about ten minutes when he looked up from the book, and said: "Don't you like this?"

"Sorry, Peter. I'm not paying much attention to it. I keep thinking about Jenny. All that last week on board ship she was with me constantly, and I must have been full of bugs all the time, because they seem to think I picked this up in Cairo."

Peter's face was a question-mark. I suddenly realized why. . . . "Of course, you don't know. Doctor Timms told me this morning what was wrong with me."

"Everything?"

"Yes."

"And all you think about is Jenny?"

"Heavens, no! . . . I thought about myself, for a very long time. It wasn't until I saw you this afternoon that I spared a thought for poor little Jenny."

Peter looked grim. "Dammit, that's one thing that hadn't occurred to me. All I can do is to go to New Zealand House and find out where her mother is. You have no idea where they were going, have you?"

"All I can remember is that Mrs Kidd was the daughter of

someone in Manchester who made raincoats or something. I think they were going there."

"That gives me a clue, anyway. I'll do what I can—and Swan, it's no earthly use you worrying. Now, story or no story? Or would you rather talk?"

"Neither. Tell me something of London."

"People, palaces, politics, or parks."

"Parks—Richmond Park, and the Thames."

He was a born raconteur: he took me through London with him. It was better than any book. As he got up to go, I said: "Could you do that more often, Peter?"

"What? Tell you about things I've seen?"

"Yes, please. I enjoyed it so much."

He bowed solemnly. "Mam'selle, you compliment me. I enjoyed talking about myself."

"You ass. Go. Good-bye."

"Huh! The 'brush-off', as they say in America. . . ." Then I felt his lips on my forehead. "I'm proud of you, Swan."

Next morning the little engine was silent from seven o'clock until ten, and at eleven my bed was wheeled out onto a verandah in the sun. By three o'clock my head ached, and I was vomiting.

"Sunstroke!" pronounced a stocky, grey-haired doctor with a foreign accent.

"But she was only out in the sun for half an hour," protested Sister.

"I do not care how long she was out, I still say, sunstroke."

Nurse Farley brought a round squashy bag, checked in black and white, and full of ice. She flattened it on my head, put something black over my eyes, and told me I must lie quietly for several hours.

When I awoke I was parched.

"Penny. Is it night?"

"Yes. You've had a wonderful sleep, for you."

"I think it's this dark thing on my eyes."

"Well, I never! I hadn't thought of that. We'll leave it there."

"I'm terribly thirsty, Penny. May I have a drink, please?"

"Yes, it's all ready. I'd better uncover you, I think." The light hurt. "There's a note on your locker for you. Do you want it now?"

"Oh, yes, please."

She opened the envelope and held a single sheet of notepaper in front of my eyes. On it was a drawing of me lying in bed, with a bag on my head, and bags under my eyes. A caption underneath, read: THE RAKE'S PROGRESS: and in writing which I recognized: "Lay off the grog—hangovers are unpleasant, and bags do not become you. Peter."

"Look at that, Penny."

"Excuse me, but I am. Couldn't help it. What's Peter like? Joyce has told me a bit about him. Is he a New Zealander?"

"No, he's English, actually. Went out to America, to relations, when his parents died. He was fifteen. They travelled about a lot, before and after the war, but Peter had always wanted to come back to England. He's terribly restless. I don't think he would ever settle down to anything for long."

"What does he do?"

"He was going to Italy to study frescoes—of all the mad things—he's crazy on them, and wants to write something about them, but at the moment he's marking time, finding out all he can about the blocking and printing and general process involved in their reproduction."

"He can certainly draw."

"Yes, he can. That's how we became friends. He picked up some drawings of mine that I had left on deck."

"Do you draw?"

"Yes." Then there was a sudden suspension of all things. "At least—I did."

"June, how are you? Honestly?"

"Fine. Really fine. Doctor Timms only told me I had infantile paralysis. He did not sign my death warrant, you know."

She laughed. "Would you like something to eat?"

"Yes, please, some pineapple." I was liberally supplied with tins of fruit by the High Commissioner. Pineapple was my favourite, and he had made it his business to find out and keep me well stocked.

85

While Penny was feeding me, Dr Black walked in behind the screens. "Headache gone?"

"Yes, thanks."

"Thank goodness for that. I think Duggy Timms is going to try and get Mr Muir to come and look at you tomorrow."

"Who's he?"

"He's the Big White Chief in orthopaedics round here."

"Oh. Bring on the black cloth, Penny. Beauty must be blotted out once more. Good night, Doctor Black."

Mr Muir did not come the following morning. He would not come until I could breathe without mechanical assistance, so, to speed things up and strengthen my respiratory muscles, I was put into the hands of the physiotherapists. They wore white smocks and white flowing veils; and they called my disease polio, not infantile paralysis. I liked that because it restored a certain amount of the conviction of my adulthood, at a time when I had to be cared for like a baby. Their job, as far as I was concerned at that moment, was to coax my breathing muscles to take over their normal function again. I never knew there were so many different ways of breathing. The efforts of the physiotherapists were unremitting, and most rewarding, because the time eventually came when I was able to breathe all day on my own, requiring the help of the pulsator at night only.

Then Dr Black came to tell me that Mr Muir definitely was coming.

"But I'm still using the Paul Brag at night."

"I know, but he's coming."

"Why does he have to come? Isn't Doctor Timms my doctor?"

"Duggy Timms is a neurologist. Your diagnosis was in his hands, because yours is a neurological disease, but your future is in the hands of an orthopaedic surgeon, who decides what course to take to put you on your feet again. He gives directions for your treatment, and the physiotherapists carry it out."

"And is this Mr Muir going to say what treatment I'm to have?"

"He's coming to look at you. That is all I know. But you'll

be in luck's way if he does take an interest in you. He is considered one of the best orthopods we've ever had."

Next morning six doctors assembled round my bed. Dr Timms, Dr Hume, and Dr Black, I knew: two of the remaining three were in white coats. The third man dominated everything. He stood taller than the other five, he was broader than any of them; and he looked impenetrable. A big head, on a big body, in a dark pin-stripe suit. He looked solid and dependable at the foot of my bed, but overpowering as he came to stand at my head.

"This is Mr Muir, June." Dr Timms's crisp voice was reassuring.

"Good morning," I said.

It fell, bright and brassy, into silence because the big man let an abstracted half-smile flicker for an instant in my direction then shut his face again. His hand shot out and turned the bedclothes back onto my stomach as he bent his head to watch my breathing. He had the most remarkable eyebrows I had ever seen. Like the outlines of miniature mountains over his eyes, they ran upwards, and angled sharply to form two bushy peaks high on his forehead: a forehead which swept down from flat, dark hair in a straight line with his nose. His lips were large, and full: his appearance fascinating, as well as frightening.

Dr Timms was studying my charts, Dr Black was chewing the inside of his cheek, and Dr Hume was standing at the foot of my bed twiddling his stethoscope.

I heard a deep intake of breath near me, and it suddenly struck me that this man bending over me had an unenviable task ahead of him. To endeavour to probe the mysteries of a bodyful of paralysed muscles was no easy matter.

"I'm going to ask you to go through a number of actions, and even if nothing moves, I want you to try. Concentrate hard, and make an effort to do what I ask. I shall only ask you to do an action once, so put everything you've got into that attempt." The rich, deep, abrupt voice that had started me on my way out of the lung.

He dug strong fingers into my stomach and told me to lift my head: he told me to laugh, to cough, and to sneeze. He gave me a pause between every movement, and when I felt his hands burrowing in some different part of my anatomy I prepared myself for a short command that would follow. He examined my face, my neck and shoulders; my arms, hands and fingers. It was not quick work, and, by the time he had reached my feet, I had to give in, because my mind refused to respond promptly to his orders.

"Sorry," I said, "I can't even think what it means to claw my toes."

"I'll give you a break. Give her a drink, nurse, and we'll start again in a few minutes."

They turned me over, and he started on my back. I was astonished to discover how difficult it was for me to think of the ordinary muscular movements that had just happened before without any thought at all. When he asked me to shrug my right shoulder I was unable to wriggle it to make sure exactly where it was in relation to my neck, but it was there somewhere, so I produced a picture of it in my mind's eye, then concentrated on endeavouring to draw the round smooth part upwards, and slightly towards, my ear. It was a sort of spatial relations test which produced considerable mental exhaustion as the examination progressed. I shut my eyes, the better to visualize the movements: thought was like a worn thread. I wondered what he thought of the inert mass as they rolled me over on my back again.

"You don't do things by halves, do you?"

At least he was not going to call black a pale shade of grey. I was grateful for his honesty. "No, I never have."

"Well, I'm afraid it's out of the frying pan into the fire— you will have to go into a plaster bed." Then to my complete surprise, that impressive but seemingly impassive orthopod said: "Will you mind very much?"

I did not mind what he wanted to do with me, because he was obviously going to "take me on", and anyway, I had no idea in the wide world what a plaster bed was. "No," I said.

Dr Black seconded me. "No, sir, she won't mind. She's used to it. She's had all manner of things in her bed."

The peaks of eyebrows rose higher: Dr Timms uttered a

remonstrative and surprised "Black!": and Dr Black looked confused, and said:

"Well, you know what I mean, sir—she's had tubes, and goodness knows what, in bed with her."

He only succeeded in getting further into the mire. Then they all laughed, and everything was back to normal.

"How did you like breathing while you were lying on your stomach?" asked a deep voice.

"Not much. It's not as easy as on my back."

"You will have to lie face downwards to have the cast made. Do you think you could manage that, for an hour?"

"I can try."

He looked at the young fair doctor. "Abbott, you take all her measurements sometime in the next two days."

"Yes, sir."

They wandered off from my bed; Dr Timms with Mr Muir in earnest conversation.

Just before lunch Dr Timms and Dr Black returned. "Now, June, you have got to be moved from here."

This was worse than anything I had ever been told. "From St Mary's, Doctor Timms? It's the only home I've got in England."

"Well, it's up to you. You can go to a big orthopaedic hospital across London—Mr Muir will look after you there— or, you can stay here. But you will have to be moved to another ward, because this one is not for orthopaedic patients."

"Won't Mr Muir look after me if I stay here?"

"Yes. He'll take care of you wherever you go."

"And you'll all still be here?"

"Yes."

"Well, what an extraordinary question to ask me. I'll stay here, please, if nobody minds. As far as I am concerned, there'll never be another hospital like St Mary's."

Dr Black laughed. "We shall have to take her along as chief barracker in the Hospital Cup Final, sir."

I looked at him. "Rugby?"

"None other. But what do you know about rugby?"

"Doctor Black! It's our national sport. Surely you've heard about our All Blacks?"

"We'll leave the rugby till later." Dr Timms broke in before Dr Black could answer. "The question, now, is where to put you. The orthopaedic ward is full at the moment, isn't it, Black?"

"Yes, sir."

"I don't suppose I'm permitted to say anything about where I'm to go, Doctor Timms?" I asked tentatively.

He looked astounded. "What have you to say?"

I did not know how to say what I had so often thought about.

"I'll be happy anywhere in St Mary's—please believe that. But there's one place, and one place only, where I'd go, if the choice were mine."

"And where is that?"

"Back to the ward, where that Sister was when I first came here."

He gave a funny little snort of incredulity. "You mean, Sister Linden, on Alexandra ward?"

"I don't know what her name is, and I don't know the name of the ward, but she's that Sister who was with me when I went into the lung."

"And you remember her all this time?"

"You couldn't forget anyone like her, Doctor Timms."

"Well!" He turned with a surprised smile, not unmixed with pleasure. "What do you think of that, Black?"

"Could it be done, sir?"

"I don't know. She could have one of my beds. It rests with Muir. If he's willing to come to Alex and see her, I don't see why she shouldn't go there—for a while, anyway." He turned to me. "It's a very busy ward, June, and noisier than this."

"I don't mind noise . . . but will it be too much trouble for Sister?"

He smiled. "I don't think anything is too much trouble for Sister Linden. I'll have a talk to her. Have we got a spare bed there, Black?"

"Yes, sir."

"Very well, I'll have her transferred before they start on her cast."

That meant that I should be on the move before two days had elapsed, and, if fate was kind, I should be moved to a place of my own choosing.

Lunch consumed, I lay contentedly contemplating my future when a voice hailed me from nearby. It was the rheumatoid arthritis patient, who was now on her feet. She had a ghastly puce-coloured dressing-gown clutched about her frame.

"Lots of Big Nobs 'ere this mornin'?"

"Yes." And to save a further round of enquiries, I added: "They're going to operate, on my brain."

"Oh, you poor dear! 'Ow you must be sufferin'." Then in a confiding tone. "And I know what sufferin's like. Nobody knows the pain I puts up with."

I tried again to shut her up. "No feeling—no pain."

"Well, that's somethink. Now, as I sez to me doctor, if only I could 'ave somethink to take me pain——"

"Please," I said, "I'm being moved away, and I've got to rest."

"Moved? Now where might you be goin' to, dearie?"

She was not to be silenced, so I decided to tell her the truth quickly, and be done. "To a ward called Alexandra, I think."

"Oh, you poor dear! I 'ad five days in there, and the Sister there's somethink dreadful."

"Sister Linden?" This was indeed news to me.

"Yes. She's a regular dragon, she is. All the time, it's orders, orders, orders."

"What rot," I said. "You've got hold of the wrong Sister. And please, I must rest."

"All right—but I'm tellin' you that she's a tartar. I was in such dreadful pain, night and day, you've no idea. Couldn't move for pain, but do you think she'd listen——"

I shut my eyes and let her drone on. Nobody could convince me that Sister Linden was a tartar, or a dragon, or that she could not listen to anyone who was really suffering.

The ballet-dancer Sister pressed my hand as we set off next morning. She had a refreshing appearance, like a dainty flower, and I was sorry to leave her. Nurse Farley, carrying my charts, went on ahead of the convoy. Two trollies, pushed by porters, followed in her wake. I lay on one, with some pink carnations Gray had brought me bunched together on my chest: my little engine, the jacket, and the contents of my locker in two pillow-cases, lay on the other. I enjoyed the trip. We went along corridors; through an overhead bridge; down in a lift; along more corridors; through a lot of glass doors; round innumerable corners; across a large hallway, up in another lift; along a short corridor; through another glass door; and there was Sister Linden. . . .

Chapter 8

THE BIRTH OF JIMMY

━━━∿∿∿ⳐᏏᏏᎧᏏᏏ∿∿∿━━━

Alexandra ward was part of a very old wing of the hospital. Its high ceiling made it look narrow: its cream and green walls, from many years of re-painting, had lost their flat polished smoothness; and, in addition to its patients, it was cram full of instrument trollies, sterilizers, swab drums, Sister's desk, and a long central table surrounded by chairs. There were three beds at the top facing down the ward, and four on either side directly opposite one another and at right angles to the ones at the top. I lay in the bottom bed, on the left-hand side, near Sister's desk. There were four windows over the beds opposite me, but there was only one through which I glimpsed the sky. The others looked onto a high, red-brick building that I assumed was another part of the hospital. After the undisturbed tenor of the penicillin ward I felt as if I had been set down in the middle of a city bus terminal at its peak hour. Through the swinging doors at either end of the ward poured a constant stream of bustling bodies; and any additional available space was filled with young men who roamed about in a dégagé manner with scribbling blocks in their hands.

"'Ullo, ducks! It's lovely to see you back."

Bending over me was a small woman with a wrinkled face. Her white smock intensified her leathery brownness and her mouth, like her eyes, seemed sunk away in furrows.

"Hullo," I said.

"I 'elped undress you, ducks, when you was first 'ere."

"Did you? Thanks very much."

"That's all right. Anytime you want anythink you just ask.

93

Lawks, ducks, I ain't never goin' to forget the time when you was cookin' in that there oven thing."

"Oven?"

"Y'know—that there box . . . they sure shut you up in that just like you was a scone loaf ready for to be baked." She stood aside. "Now 'ere's one of the young gentlemens what 'as come to talk to you. I'll be goin'. See you later."

A young man with fluffy brown hair took her place. "I'm one of the students here. I've got to write up a case history of you, and I expect from the look of all this"—his fingers flicked the pages of the charts hanging on my locker—"you will be seeing quite a bit of me."

"Do you have to write up case histories on all the patients?"

"No. We each have certain ones allotted to us. I was due for the next of Duggy Timms's and I guess I'd better start reading what's already been written."

He sat down on the locker and bent his head over the accumulated mass of my medical reports.

"You won't have much of an opinion of England?"

"I haven't formed any opinion of it at all, as I haven't seen it. But if it's anything like the people I've met since I've been here, it must be a wonderful country."

"So you think we're all right?"

"The English people I've come across—yes. Absolutely tops. But then I really can't judge by ordinary standards."

"No, I suppose not. I say . . . do you read or anything?"

"Actually, I love it, but I can't read now because I can't hold a book."

"But surely there's some sort of stand that could hold a book in front of you?" He was frowning. "Look—I'll see if I can dig one up, if you like."

"I should like, very much indeed. But don't go to any bother."

He waved a vague hand. "Oh, no bother." He looked up as Nurse Farley appeared.

"Doctor Hume is over on the men's side," she said.

He jumped up quickly. "Thanks, nurse."

She turned to me. "Mr Muir has just rung up. He wants you

94

to try and spend part of the night out of the Paul Brag because you won't be able to wear it when you're in your plaster bed."

"When are they making it?"

"I saw your name up on the list outside the main theatre as I came past this morning."

"Theatre?"

"Yes, you have to go to the operating theatre to have it made, you know, and as it's the main one I expect the gallery will be open."

"The gallery will be open! What on earth does that mean?"

"That there'll be students watching."

"Help!"

"You don't mind, do you?"

"No. I'm getting hardened to exposure now."

"You never did mind, did you?"

"I certainly did. I loathed it at first—I was awfully embarrassed and humiliated, but it had to be, so that was all there was to it . . . and then you and Penny were so good the way you handled me that I stopped feeling so awful about it. And it must have been a lot worse for you."

"Do you still mind? Be honest."

"It depends who it is. I don't with you—not the least bit."

"Well, have a drink. We'll try and toughen your hide that way."

Despite noise and bustle I was happy because I could see Sister at her desk or in the ward. As she sat writing she looked up over her horn-rimmed glasses and smiled. Presently she came over to my bed.

"Well, June, how do you like being back?"

"Very much—but it's all so different from the other ward."

"Yes. I hope the noise isn't going to be too much for you."

"Oh, no, I'm sure it won't. . . . Sister, did you know what was wrong with me when I was here before?"

"Yes."

"I wonder why it didn't occur to me? Silly, wasn't it?"

She fidgeted with her glasses. "To be perfectly honest, it did occur to you. Don't you remember?"

"No—when?"

"The day we moved you in here, from the small ward. You called me over to you, and said quite distinctly, 'Sister, have I got infantile paralysis?' "

"Did I really! And what did you say?"

She gave a short, apologetic laugh. "I looked you straight in the eye, and said, very decidedly, 'No, June, you haven't,' because I thought you were too ill to know."

"Sounds incredible. I don't remember a thing about it. . . . Thank you, anyway, for all that you did for me then."

She twisted her glasses in her fingers. "There is no need for thanks. We are here to help sick people."

I went to sleep that night for the first time without my engine. During the day I was able to help my muscles by thinking what they had to do to keep breath in my body, but we were not sure what would happen when sleep had taken away conscious control. Penny was on guard. All went well until I became aware of a tall object propped against the foot of my bed. It was draped in something white, two pieces of which extended outwards from the top of it. To my consternation these began to move, the whole macabre effect being that of some monster dissecting an imaginary corpse. I was bemused with sleep, and it was seconds before I rallied sufficiently to realize what it was.

"Doctor," I whispered. "Oh, you did give me a fright."

Penny jumped to her feet as the tall, fair Abbott came to the head of the bed.

"I'm terribly sorry, but I'm glad you're awake. I want to measure your length and width. I was attempting to gauge them without waking you. It won't take a minute."

He produced what looked to me like a piece of string; asked Penny to hold one end at my head, while he pulled it taut then tied a knot in it at my feet. He ran a measuring tape across my shoulders, waist, and hips, then down the length of my legs; scribbled with a pencil in a little book, and was gone. It was midnight.

Penny put my strait-jacket on, started the little engine chugging, and had just finished giving me a drink when a nurse crept in behind the screens. "What is it, nurse?" Penny asked.

"Operating theatre have just rung and want to know if she is the patient that the plaster bed's being made for tomorrow?"

"Yes, she is."

The nurse turned to me. "Do you know how long you are?"

"Approximately—why?"

"Well O.T. have received an order from Mr Muir's houseman to prepare gauze for a plaster cast eighty-four inches in length."

"Eighty-four inches! I'm not as long as that."

Penny raised a silencing finger to her lips. "Not too loud, old thing."

"Sorry. I know I'm tall, but surely I haven't grown to that length."

"What is your height?"

"Five feet nine and a half as far as I know."

"Good—oh, thanks."

Penny told me, as she attended to me next morning, that Dr Abbott had remained adamant and all through the early hours of the morning the night staff in O.T. had been busily occupied cutting yards of gauze into eighty-four-inch lengths which were then split longitudinally at one end to accommodate my legs.

At 9.30 a.m. a theatre porter came to collect me. As he wheeled the trolley along the main corridor leading to the theatre we were met by an intensely appetizing odour. "What's that smell?" I enquired.

"Oh, that—that's the soup for the surgeons' lunch."

Lucky surgeons, I thought: then I was in the theatre, my face shiny from the morning's wash, and my hair completely covered with a close-fitting rubber bathing cap. I was not a little apprehensive. An operating theatre, to any patient, is a place of wonder. Everything ran on oiled wheels. Footsteps were soft, voices were lowered, and the atmosphere was one of super cleanliness; the chromium trolleys shone, the overhanging lights were polished to a mirror-like brilliance, and the hundreds of oddly shaped instruments glistened. Everything centred like a powerful spot-light on the raised, tomb-like slab that was the operating table. It was the focus for hundreds of pairs of eyes from the students' gallery; standing guard over it was the anaesthetists' conglomerate apparatus, and trolleys were within reaching distance of it. A student in a long green robe tied in the middle and gaping at the back, an ugly flat turban, and a mask, stood watch.

"You the patient from Alex?"

"Yes."

"Since when have they admitted children there?"

"How old do you think I am?"

"About twelve."

He did not look as if he was long past adolescence himself. I felt indignant, but did not say so, for everyone arrived at once and diverted my attention. Mr Muir and assistants, Sister Theatre, students everywhere, and a bevy of nurses who settled themselves around a bath that was standing on the floor. The night of the Fancy Dress Ball on board ship flashed through my mind. Mr Muir and his entourage would have taken all the prizes. Their draperies consisted of a conglomeration of tight-fitting turbans, masks, long gowns of various shapes and sizes, rubber aprons, rubber gloves, rubber leg-guards, and galoshes. There was a whisper from the gallery:

"Expecting rain?"

I hoped the big man had not heard it, but nothing escaped him. I could see no more than his eyes: he was not amused. Without more ado they began to strip blankets and clothes off me. The student who had assumed me to be "about twelve" stood nonplussed.

"Sorry, June," said Mr Muir, "but this is necessary, you know."

Eight of them picked me up completely naked, flipped me over like a pancake to place me face downwards on the operating table, over which a waterproof sheet was spread. Directly in front of my eyes was the green-robed student sitting behind two cylinders of carbon dioxide. That was something I could not understand. Three nurses hovered over the bath, which stood at the top and a little to the right of the table. The eighty-four-inch lengths of gauze, with Sister in charge, were piled to the right of the bath. On the left of the table stood a large jar of what appeared to me to be petroleum jelly. The doctors plunged their rubber-gloved hands into the jar, bringing forth great greasy masses of jelly which they proceeded to rub all over me. They jellied my ears, round my neck, over the bathing cap, under my arms, over and down the entire length of my body and legs, and between my toes. Had it not been for the smell of the surgeon's soup, which kept wafting through the open door, the petroleum would have been unbearable. There was scarcely a pause.

"Is the bath ready, nurse?"

"Yes, sir."

"Right. The first layer please."

Sister lifted one of the lengths of gauze; the nurses dipped it in the bath, which apparently contained a concentrated solution of plaster and water; then handed the dripping sodden mass to the doctors. They slapped it straight onto my jellied back, over my jellied bathing-cap, round and over my jellied toes. I thought of the old man, who lived next to us as children, telling us how he used to go and cut a hole in the ice in the middle of winter and, when he struck water, drop naked into the hole. Again and again they slid their rubbery hands up and down the length of my body, smoothing and patting that plaster strip until there was no evidence of a crease or an air bubble.

"Next layer please."

I wanted to see how many more layers there were, but I had to keep my eyes shut most of the time for fear of plaster dripping into them.

"Are you all right under there?"

By this time the weight of sodden plaster had begun to solidify. I could do nothing but think. I thought I was all right, but could not speak. Someone bent down and attempted to peer up at me.

"From what I can see of her, sir, she's still breathing."

"Right. Watch her."

The slapping, patting, smoothing went on and on. I stopped counting after the tenth "next layer please" because my face was burning, I was puffing quickly, and had started making my peculiar screeching noises.

"Can she last out?"

"No, sir."

"Put the mask on her. You will have to hold it on." A muzzle was thrust up into my face and I heard a sizzle of escaping gas. I seemed to breathe faster than ever. "Keep at it, June. We shall not be long."

While meditating on the horrors of being buried alive, I realized that the riddle of the eighty-four inches was being solved. These strips of gauze, saturated with plaster, were being taken from my eyebrows up and over my head, down my back to my heels, up and over the soles of my feet to cover my toes. Not excluding the two or three inches that continually flapped against my tightly shut eyes and trickled down my cheeks, the whole strip must necessarily have measured that length.

"How is she?"

"Breath coming very fast, sir."

"As long as it's coming."

There was a further period of pummelling, sloshing and slapping; a short pause while the top layer solidified; and the entire encumbrance was lifted from my back. I lay, gasping for breath, while Sister and the nurses chipped pieces of plaster off me, and endeavoured to remove the remains of the jelly. For all its obnoxiousness that jelly was a godsend, as it prevented the plaster from adhering to my flesh.

I opened my eyes to see plaster everywhere. I remembered the whisper from the gallery. Certainly everyone and everything looked as if a plaster cloud had burst upon them. I was turned over, lifted back onto the trolley, and covered up. For the first time I saw my plaster bed. It was a masterpiece. Smooth, and beautifully moulded, it lay on a trolley while Mr Muir drew a circle on it from the bottom of the spine, halfway out on either hip, and a little below the join of the legs. He turned to Nurse Farley as she came into the theatre.

"Take her down immediately, nurse, and ask Sister to give her some oxygen."

"Yes, sir."

The porter wheeled the trolley away with Nurse Farley walking beside it. I was too blown to ask her why she had come.

I was glad to be back in the ward with Sister Linden, a warm bed, and some oxygen.

"Nurse, fill some hotties, she's like ice. We shall have to leave her covered with all this until she has had a rest."

I slept until mid-afternoon.

"Nurse, I'm thirsty. May I have a drink, please?"

Nurse Farley jumped up. "Yes, of course. What a sleep you've had!"

"Nurse Farley, do the surgeons always have soup for their lunch?"

"Soup, June! What on earth are you talking about?"

"Well, there was a most appetizing smell up in the corridor leading to theatre—the porter says it is soup for the surgeons."

Nurse looked embarrassed, but vouchsafed no answer as she helped me with my drink. Sister came over while I was having it.

"Feeling better?"

"I never felt bad—only tired. . . . Sister, have you ever smelt anything as you pass along the corridor to the main operating theatre?"

"Yes, it's always there. Why?"

"Well, Nurse Farley just looked uncomfortable when I mentioned that the porter had told me that it was soup for the surgeons' lunch. Is there anything strange about it?"

Sister's merry brown eyes danced. "June, you idiot! Of course it isn't soup. That smell comes from the huge coppers where they burn the operational offal . . . however, I did not come over here to tell you that. Mr Johns rang this afternoon while you were away. He says he will come and see you this evening, instead of this afternoon, and he said to tell you that Jenny is quite all right."

"Thank goodness for that."

"And one of the students has brought in an amazing contrivance for holding books."

"Where is it, Sister?"

"He is coming back shortly, to adjust it for you."

The book stand was a mystery of arms that shot out at all angles, and a small rotating ball in its stem that enabled it to be tipped in any direction. There were plenty of people within hailing distance to turn pages for me.

Peter grinned when he saw it. "You are shockingly——"

"I know. I know quite well—spoilt. I am, and I love it."

Then he told me that Jenny's mother on her way from England to South Africa had called at New Zealand House; had been told of my illness; and had immediately taken Jenny to a doctor. The results of the tests had come through that morning: there was no trace of polio.

"Her mother is writing to you. She was sorry she couldn't get up to see you," said Peter.

"Never mind, as long as Jenny is well. . . . Peter, now that I'm on the 'up and up' as they say here, why don't you go to Italy?"

"I'll see you into this plaster thing first, Swan, then perhaps, I'll be off."

"And, Peter . . . why don't you find yourself a little brunette with a good pair of legs?"

His head went back as he burst into gales of laughter. "Are you suggesting that I spend the remainder of the evening in Piccadilly?" He pulled his flop of black hair over his forehead, half-closed his eyes, put one hand on his hip, took a few mincing steps, and let out a low wolf howl.

"Peter, stop it! They'll think you are crazy."

All through that night I slept, for the first time, without any mechanical respiratory aid. The following morning I discovered I could laugh. It was a silly, apologetic sound, like a trickle of water hiccoughing down a drain-pipe; but it was a laugh. I laughed all day until Nurse begged me to stop.

"You'll kill yourself."

"Nice way to die, Nurse, ha, ha, ha."

They called me the girl with the drain-pipe laugh, but they kept me at it. They told me funny stories and performed antics in front of me, both of which were quite unnecessary because

I laughed at anything that day. Dr Black laughed with me, or at me.

"Must have been all that panting under the plaster yesterday."

"By Jove, yes—it could have started something. Try and cough."

I produced a muffled sound that might have been anything. "Why can't I cough?"

"Because the muscles of your stomach are paralysed. That is why you haven't been able to laugh, or blow your nose, or cough, or sneeze. But now you've started laughing it ought to strengthen the muscles and help the other activities along. Laugh as much as you can."

I did, until Nurse Farley told me that she was leaving me: that was no laughing matter. "Won't I ever see you again, nurse?"

"Yes. I'd like to come and visit you. But I'll not be looking after you any more. I have to go on theatre—another nurse is replacing me. You'll be a good girl, won't you?"

"I hope so."

"Very well, then—laugh."

It was useless to lament, and unworthy of this quiet girl who had done more than I cared to think about for my bodily and mental comfort.

My plaster bed arrived from the drying-room three days later. It occasioned many laughs, many admiring exclamations, and much discussion because Alexandra was a medical and neurological ward and a plaster bed was something unique. There was a large hole cut in the bottom of it where I had seen Mr Muir drawing the lines while I was still in theatre. As Dr Black entered the ward, preparatory to conducting his morning round, he spotted my cast lying, recumbent and unashamedly naked, on an unoccupied bed across the ward.

"Good Lord! What's this?"

A staff nurse was filing the glass cork off a small bottle. She looked up briefly. "That's June's plaster bed."

"Why isn't she in it?"

"I've got to line it."

"What are you going to line it with?"

"With elephant plaster."

"With what?"

"Elephant plaster."

"Nurse, are you trying to be funny?"

"No, I'm not given to being funny at other people's expense."

Dr Black eyed her for a moment, then grinned. "I believe you. Could you show me a piece of this elephant plaster?"

Nurse duly produced what proved to be a smooth felt-like material approximately a quarter of an inch in thickness, with a layer of some exceedingly adhesive property on one side. This felt nurse cut into lengths to fit the interior of the cast. They were then stuck in firmly, providing a soft warm protection against the otherwise cold plaster. It was a painstaking task and nurse was justifiably proud of the result. My bed stood against the wall, looking like the posterior of an Egyptian mummy waiting for its frame.

This was an oblong, wooden box, six and a half feet long, two feet wide, and a foot high. It had no top or lid, but across the inside of it, at intervals of eighteen inches, were staves or cross bars shaped to accommodate the cast and to ensure that it remained fixed in the correct position. A square hole was cut in the right side of the frame corresponding to the hole in the plaster bed. I was put on the trolley while my bed was stripped of mattresses, pillows, sheets, and blankets. Planks were fitted over the wire wove, the frame was fitted over the planks, the cast was fitted into the frame, and I was fitted into the cast. A long white gown draped the visible portions of my body and over this was thrown a sheet and some blankets.

The first night I found my new bed cold: the second night it was hard, as well as cold: the third night it was hard, cold, and uncomfortably intimate: the fourth night the hardness, the coldness and the intimacy were still there, but I began to acknowledge its virtues. It was no longer necessary for three nurses to clutch what they could of the flaccid mass of my body to put me on a bedpan. It was no longer possible to roll me over to rub my back, because I was fixed in the shell; but the greatest relief of all was to have no sore or aching muscles because I lay encased in a mould that allowed complete relaxation to every one of them.

I took off my hat to the big man. Apart from physical comfort, I was relieved of a considerable amount of mental distress because of the simplified nursing. The hole cut in the frame corresponding with the one in the cast facilitated manœuvres pertaining to bedpans, backs, and washes. But the beauty of the cast lay not in its design or its comfort, but in its *raison d'être*: it meant that my spine was being kept straight until such time as the muscles in my trunk were fit enough to go back to work. Its task was a responsible and honourable one. It made my shell worthy of some distinction which would separate it from the category of inanimate things: so I called it Jimmy.

Chapter 9

JUGS, PLUGS, AND POISON

D uring the afternoon of the fifth day in Jimmy's company Peter came to tell me that he was leaving for Italy. I was glad. Although I knew that I should miss him beyond telling, I thought he deserved a break from the difficult task of trying to be all things at once to me, mother, father, sister, and friend. The fact that he was happy to leave me also made me glad, because it meant that I must be looking more like my former self.

"Peter, you—um, haven't got a mirror on you, have you?"

"A mirror! What on earth——"

"I know. It's just a whim, and a vain one at that, but I haven't seen my face since I was in that hostel in Holborn."

"Good heavens, I don't suppose you have. Sorry, but I haven't got one on me. Anyway, you look just the same as you always did, except that you're a bit thinner and your eyes look bigger."

"Did I look very sick, at first?"

"You! Look sick? Not once. You smelt, that's all."

"Smelt! You horror."

"You asked for it." He grinned. "But don't you go getting any ideas that you can lie in bed looking ethereal, because it's impossible. If anything, your eyes get brighter and your cheeks pinker."

He turned, and in one stride was at the bedside of the patient next to me.

"Excuse me, madam, but have you a mirror I could borrow for a few minutes, please? The young woman next to you is suffering from a chronic disease of the fair sex—vanity."

He was back with a small powder compact.

"This will be quite enough to begin with. If you've forgotten what you look like, you will have to take it in easy stages." He held the small disc of mirror above me.

The first thing I noticed was that I had lost all my customary tan. I had never seen myself without some vestige of it, and I should not have minded its loss had it been replaced by an interesting pallor. But it was not. I was what could only be described as pink and white, blue-eyed, and babyish.

"Ugh. Thanks all the same, Peter."

"What's the matter? Don't you know yourself?"

"I'm so pink and white and namby-pamby looking. Just put a bonnet on me, will you—with rosebuds and blue bows——"

"And give you the treatment?"

We were both laughing as Sister came and stood on the other side of the bed. "Whatever is she up to?"

"Getting an eyeful of what we have to gaze at, day after day, Sister."

She laughed outright.

"You can both afford to laugh. You have a beautifully tanned skin, Sister, and Peter would never go this soppy colour."

"But, my dear, you will keep that till the day you die."

"Heaven forbid . . ."

Peter had returned the mirror and come back to the bed. "I must away, my dear. I'm off to Italy for a while, Sister. Good-bye."

They shook hands. "I'll write to you, Swan, and let you know how many brunettes I'm dating. Good-bye." His lips were on my forehead.

"Good-bye, Peter. Have a lovely trip." His long legs took his flop of shiny black hair quickly out of sight. "He's a wonderful friend, isn't he, Sister?"

"Yes. I don't think I shall ever forget the first time he came to see you. We told him he could come whenever he wished, and he unfortunately arrived the second time just as we were putting you into the lung. He looked worse than you did, as far as colour was concerned." Then she gave me a very direct look from those brown eyes of hers. "And while we are on the subject of your appearance—you have got very thin, and weak, and Mr Muir wants to start you on some strenuous daily treatment. You will never be able to stand up to it unless you eat."

"But I do eat, Sister."

"You don't eat, June. You pick, and that is not enough. You must get stronger if the physiotherapists are going to do anything with you, so you must eat more."

"I shall try, Sister."

"We'll make it a little and often. I'll get Mrs Venning to make you an omelette now, and I want you to promise me that you will eat it all."

"Even if I burst?"

"Yes."

"I promise."

A plump, jolly nurse arrived with my omelette which was delicious, until I was halfway through it: then it became a soggy, tasteless mass that had to be swallowed because I had given my promise to Sister. I had by no means recovered from the effects of what I thought was an overloaded stomach when a slim, but strong-featured girl arrived with my supper—which name, I had learned, was given to an evening meal in England. I had been briefed on this nurse. She had only arrived on the ward that afternoon but she had received previous training in a fever hospital, so that polios, plaster beds, and their accompanying difficulties were well known to her. I realized that it was necessary that I should eat, but I rebelled in the name of my stretched stomach as Nurse placed the plate on my locker. It contained lettuce, beetroot, and a tender cut of the breast of a chicken which she proceeded to carve into cubes preparatory to feeding me.

"Nurse, I'm not hungry."

She must have guessed that it was my habitual cry, for she ignored it completely and concentrated on putting things into my mouth every time I opened it to complain. This was my first encounter with such determined tactics. Her very silence infuriated me. After the fourth grudging swallow I uttered vehement protest. She merely held the fork over my mouth until it was conveniently open, then slipped the food in. Her colour was mounting a little, but still she said nothing. I ceased my protestations, clenched my teeth, and pressed my lips together. The fork hovered, but now above a shut mouth. I spared no thought for my shameful behaviour because it was a meal, as Sister well knew, that I usually enjoyed, but I was so enraged by the deliberation with which it was being rammed down my throat that I quietly made up my mind to have no more. The fork, with a piece of chicken attached, was still poised above my mouth. She was forced to speak.

"Will you open your mouth and eat this, please?"

"No," I muttered through clenched teeth.

"But, you must eat it."

"Why?"

"Because you've hardly had any of it yet."

"I've had quite sufficient, thank you." I was staring at the ceiling.

"You've made up your mind you're not going to try, haven't you?" Nurse's voice was cold with anger.

"Yes." A monosyllable, but enough for another attempt to be made to force the chicken into my mouth. But I have strong teeth. After further unsuccessful tussles she retreated to the kitchen, bearing the greater portion of my supper on the plate. She returned with some jelly which had been made from crystals that my mother had sent for me, knowing how fond I was of it.

"Are you going to try and eat this?"

I wanted that jelly. "No."

"But Sister tells me you like it." The spoon began to menace my mouth.

"I don't always like it."

At that she flared. "You—you. You are the most obstinate person I have ever met." Her eyes flashed and her face was red.

"And you are the most obstinate one I have ever met. I am not going to eat anything more, and nothing you can do will make me."

I was seething with unreasonable and unpardonable rage. Nurse flounced away, leaving the jelly on the locker.

That evening, while Sister was off duty, Staff Nurse came to my bedside. "Enjoy your supper?"

"No." I was peevish. "That self-inflated pre-train coming here with her ideas of how a patient should be treated."

Nurse evinced surprise. "But she's spent three years attending cases in plaster beds, and we thought she would be just the one for you."

"Is she on tomorrow morning?"

"Yes, why?"

"Because, please, Nurse, if you've got any bright ideas about sending her to me for morning washes, dismiss them—please. I couldn't bear it."

The following morning a nurse came in behind the screen, carrying a large bowl of warm water. It was none other than my combatant of the previous evening. She stripped what bed-clothes lay on me and set to work. There was no denying her efficiency in washing patients in plaster casts: that was the most thorough and enjoyable wash I had ever experienced since Jimmy's intimacy had made such ministrations awkward. She was so quickly finished and gone that I had no time in which to murmur a word of thanks. I felt a heel.

On her morning round Sister beamed broadly as she greeted me: "You're looking very cheerful."

"Yes, Sister, I've had such a good wash. I feel a new person."

"Who washed you?"

"Nurse—um—Nurse . . . you know, the new one, the pre-train."

"Nurse Sheldon?"

"Yes."

A little later my enemy-turned-friend came round, dusting lockers. I felt foolish and diffident. She fiddled about unnecessarily for some moments then, as I was endeavouring to overcome my stupid fit of embarrassment, she spoke:

"Sister tells me you enjoyed your wash."

"Yes, I did. I was just summoning sufficient courage to thank you, and to apologize for that unforgivable display of stubbornness last evening. I don't know what possessed me, I'm awfully sorry."

"I am, too." She sounded relieved, and for the first time we looked at each other without enmity. Without waiting to be asked she set my book on the reading stand, pushed my flowers where I could see them, and brushed some odd strands of hair off my forehead.

"Call me, if you want anything."

She had passed to the next locker leaving me to reflect on my infantile behaviour of the previous evening. It was her first experience of a hospital like St Mary's. Everything was strange, and when Sister Linden told any nurse, new or not, to see that a patient ate all her supper, she spoke in a tone which left no doubt that she did not intend Nurse to return with an un-emptied plate. I was wholly to blame for the fracas.

Then the door swung open to admit Dr Hume, who had been away on holiday for a fortnight. He pulled up short.

"Good morning, June—what, in the name of fortune, have they got you in now?"

"Good morning, Doctor Hume. It's my plaster bed, and its name is Jimmy."

"Why?"

"That is a long, and involved, story."

"I suppose I'm allowed to inspect said Jimmy?"

He ran his finger down Jimmy's length, then proceeded to poke round, pry into, and explore him in detail. He rapped along the side of the frame support with his knuckles until he came to a space. He bent his head to the level of the square hole in the box.

"What's this for?"

I said nothing. He peered in, to be met, I can only assume, by the remarkable sight of two partially exposed bottom-cheeks protruding through the hole in Jimmy's back. He came up, a grin on his handsome face. One arm was thrust through the hole in the frame and I felt a gentle pat on my posterior.

"You must have been a beautiful baby, June."

Dr Meiklejohn appeared at the foot of my bed. "What's all this about June being a beautiful baby?"

Dr Hume was still smiling. "Just a personal affair, old chap —oh, good morning, Sister Linden."

"Good morning, Doctor Hume. Our patient looks well, don't you think?"

"Never better. May we start some lectures on her, Sister?"

"Yes, but Doctor Timms is doing one this morning, and the physiotherapists are starting in earnest now, so you will have to——"

"Book in advance, as it were?"

"Yes. And I warn you, she'll drink in every word that comes out of your mouth."

"Oh, she's one of those, is she?"

"Yes." Sister smiled indulgently while I protested.

"Dash it all, Doctor Hume, you can't expect me to lie here absolutely deaf to what is being said . . . it's jolly interesting. I'm quite pally with duodenal ulcers, hearts, chests, and rheumatoids."

Two physiotherapists arrived, carrying between them a square box with a lot of electrical leads attached to it.

"How long shall we have before Doctor Timms arrives, Sister?"

"Not long."

"Well, we'd best leave the electrical part and do her massage and her passive movements."

"Just do something to make her really hungry."

Dr Hume turned to Sister. "Hungry? Won't she eat?"

"Yes, I'll eat anything now, Sister, if you send Nurse Sheldon to feed me. I'd never refuse her."

"Why Nurse Sheldon?"

"Surely, Sister, you know what happened last night at supper? I behaved shockingly."

"Did you? This is news to me."

I told them as briefly as I could, and Sister had only time in which to look, but not voice, her displeasure at my conduct before Staff Nurse came to tell her that Dr Timms had arrived.

The physiotherapists put my legs back in the cast with a resigned sigh, gathered up their paraphernalia, and departed. Dr Meiklejohn disappeared, and Dr Hume joined Dr Timms and the students. They crowded round my bed. Dr Timms stood at the top right-hand side, with Dr Black beside him: Dr

Hume stood opposite, and the lecture began. It was the first of many.

A large portion of what was said was beyond my comprehension. I knew less than the average person about anatomy, physiology, the nature, cause, and treatment of diseases, or anything connected with the theory of medicine as a whole. But I did make an attempt to understand as much as I could of my own disease, dismissing that which was not completely comprehensible to my lay mind for fear of misconstruing what I had only partially grasped. After listening to the divergent views of many different lecturers I attempted to simplify the jargon in order to understand this disease, which they called "anterior poliomyelitis".

The best analogy I could think of was a simple household commodity, an electric jug. An electric jug is used many times every day—I doubt if anyone could enumerate, off hand, just how many. The process is so habitual, and in consequence so automatic, that the boiling of water in the jug requires no more conscious effort for us than crossing our legs, stooping to admire a flower in the garden, or blowing our noses. The jug is full of water: somewhere attached to it is a flex, which leads to an electrical plug in the wall. From this plug a current of electricity is continually conducted along the flex, and into the jug. The water reacts to the contact of the electrically stimulated element, and eventually boils. So with our mechanism.

Situated in the centre of our back is our spine, dotted with hundreds of cells. These are the electrical plugs in the wall. From each cell there is a nerve pathway, or flex that leads to a muscle. Just as the wall-plug transmits electricity along the flex and into the jug, so the cells transmit impulses along the nerve pathway and into the muscles. The muscles react to the stimulus of the impulse, and they move. We have hundreds of such systems in our bodies, and all these plugs, or cells, are concentrated in the spine, from which the entire central nervous system radiates. Our flexes, or nerve tracks, vary in size and length according to the situation and strength of the muscles which they feed—there are hundreds of individual muscles and parts of muscles, hundreds of nerve tracks, and consequently hundreds of cells; for every muscle must have its separate transmitting mechanism.

I wondered why more things did not go wrong with people's bodies, when there was so much delicate machinery that could be unwittingly abused, and when I considered the mishaps that so frequently befall electrical appliances. If the jug is at fault, it can be repaired; if the flex is at fault, that also can be repaired; but if the supply of electricity from the wall-plug ceases, little can be done about it. The power has been cut, the flex and the jug stand idle: they are useless.

The same applies to muscles. If we cannot move a perfectly normal-looking toe, it means that something is at fault, the muscle, the nerve track, or the cell. A torn or injured muscle will mend; an injured nerve track can often be restored; but a diseased cell will never, never, repair itself. There is no way known to medicine of rebuilding it; so if the cells in our spine are injured—as they are in infantile paralysis—the power has been cut, transmission of stimuli through the nerve flex to the muscle ceases, and the latter lie idle. Polio is not a disease of the muscles, nor a disease of the nerve track, but a disease that attacks the cells in the spine. It is because of the impairment of those cells that the muscles refuse to react and the victim is unable to move. The cells lie embedded in the soft, grey matter surrounding the spinal cord, encased in the bony structure of the vertebrae, or spine. Hence the pathological explanation of poliomyelitis, as "an inflammation of the anterior part of the grey matter of the spinal cord".

The reason for the qualification, "anterior", arises from the fact that the cells injured are the front ones only. The posterior are not attacked by the virus, and it is because of this that the disease affects the function of motion, but not that of sensation —anterior cells being concerned with motivation, posterior with the sense of feeling. This differentiation between move-ment and feeling explained to me one of the principal reasons for my disregard, in making my own diagnosis, of the possi-bility of infantile paralysis. I had always thought that a para-lysed muscle also lacked sensation: I knew that I could feel, and concluded that it was only a question of time and strength before I would be fully mobile once more. But that was not so. I never lost my sense of feeling, despite a body full of immobilized muscles.

It was agreed unanimously that I must have become infected by the virus while I was in either Cairo or Port Said, as the incubation period was reckoned to be nine or ten days. The cause of it all was the elusive virus, too small to be seen under an ordinary microscope, but which, I gathered, two men had managed to isolate in a fairly pure state, thus opening up the way for more extensive polio research; all of which is concerned with the problem of finding the clue that will mean death to the disease.

The amount of paralysis that will be suffered by any polio victim depends entirely on the number of cells inflamed by the virus, and the extent of that inflammation. During the infectious stages every single cell in the body appears to have been attacked, for the victim seems unable to move anything, but after a period of a week or two the inflammation dies down, and doctors endeavour to estimate the principal damage evidenced by external immobility. When there is paralysis of one limb only—a leg or an arm—it means that the virus has affected only those cells which supply the impulses to that particular group of muscles, before the natural forces at work in the body have been able to overcome, and stifle, the spreading of the disease. Sometimes the virus has sufficient time, before it is destroyed, to attack all the cells situated in the lower region of the vertebrae, in which case paralysis of both legs will result. If it travels a little higher, the consequent immobility will extend from the waist downwards. In acute cases it contaminates cells up and down the entire length of the spine, often involving respiratory muscles, and necessitating the use of an iron lung.

But the virus plays a game of hit and miss. It is capricious, wilful, and conforms to no systematized pattern of attack. It does not start its work at the bottom of the vertebrae, and continue upwards, nor does it start at the top, and work downwards. It poisons where it pleases. From a group of cells in the same section of the spine it may attack one or two, and leave the others undamaged, with the result that the victim suffers paralysis of one side of the neck, but not the other. There are other diseases that paralyse, but none so arbitrarily as polio. Sometimes only a part of the cell is damaged, leaving an active, but considerably weakened, transmitting station, that supplies about half the full amount of stimulus to the muscle, which is consequently reduced to half its normal power. There was no polio epidemic to spread, and thus weaken, the force of the virus when I was attacked: mine was a sporadic case that gave free rein to a vigorous and concentrated onslaught. It was a case of "all or nothing".

Dr Timms lectured on the signs, symptoms, and diagnosis of the disease because he was a neurologist, and any disease connected with the central nervous system is a neurological one. Dr Hume concentrated, principally, on the effects of inter-costal paralysis or paralysis of the muscles controlling the respiratory mechanism, and the work of the iron lung. Mr Muir was concerned with remedial treatment, the different methods of inducing paralysed muscles to function again, the possi-bilities of recovery, and the effect of temporary and residual paralysis in what he termed a "quadraplegic polio"—one hav-ing paralysis of the trunk and all four limbs.

I experienced considerable difficulty following the big man's lectures, because I knew none of the correct anatomical names for the various muscles. I had no way of knowing that, when he talked about my gastrocnemus, he was merely referring to one of the muscles that was required to point my foot. At the end of his second lecture he looked down at me, with a smile:

"Mental fog?"

"Yes. Shouldn't be listening, I suppose."

"No harm in you listening. I suggest you learn your anatomy. It would be quite a good idea if you did. Your physiotherapists will help you. Learn the names of the muscles, their point of origin and insertion, and their use, then you will not be led into the mistake of making trick movements—a failing with all paralytics. In the early stages it reduces chances of normal recovery. Get one of the students to lend you a book on anatomy. It will be interesting from our point of view, as well as yours, and perhaps we shall be able to fill in a blank on your chart."

"What blank?"

A gruff rumble of laughter came from him. "Next to your intelligence."

That evening I asked Dr Black what the big man meant. He produced a file of notes which he brought back to my bedside. I glanced quickly at the top of the sheet, then down. Set out on it were all the usual requirements for a medical case history: name, age, address, religion, symptoms, general physical appearance, intelligence, temperature and pulse etc. on admission. Dr Black's finger was pointing to the word "intelligence". In the space next to it was a question mark. "Who filled this in?" I asked.

"I did."

"Can't you make up your mind about my intelligence?"

"No. We're still querying it."

"After all these months?" I was amazed.

"Yes."

"But that's stupid. I got back to normal ages ago. I shan't change—mentally, I mean."

He laughed. "To tell you the truth, I'd forgotten all about it. It will have to stand as it is—but if you'll give me one of those home-made ginger-nuts your mother sends to you, I'll see what I can do to make some amends in the pages further on." He sat munching ginger-nuts while he scribbled in the mass of notes, until Nurse Sheldon came with my supper. "Mm—the Lady with the Shovel—I'd best be off." He grabbed another biscuit before he went.

Nurse looked after him. "What's he eating?"

"Ginger-nuts. My mother sent them over. Would you like some, nurse?"

"I can't eat your biscuits. He shouldn't either; they're sent for you. What are you going to eat when you're hungry?"

"I never am, not really."

"You will, when they start packing stout into you."

"Stout!"

"Yes, there's a whole crateful of it out in the kitchen for

you. Doctor Timms, Mr Muir, and Sister, had a round-table conference about your appetite, and they've decided that stout is the answer. You've got to have a bottle a day." She giggled. "I hope you don't get tight."

"My poor stomach will."

"Well, just tighten it up on some of this, will you?"

She held a forkful of food over my mouth. It was not refused.

Sister came to the bedside as Nurse was cleaning my face. "I'm very pleased with the way you are eating, June."

"You can thank Nurse Sheldon, Sister—and by the way, what's all this about stout?"

"You are going to have a bottle a day." She looked at me dubiously. "You couldn't manage a glassful, now?"

"Actually, Sister, I'd rather have a cup of tea, but I'll try the stout if you want me to."

"Well, you weren't supposed to start having it until to-morrow so we shall leave it at that. I'll make you a little pot of tea, myself. You haven't had any since you've been here, have you?"

"No, it's the first time I've felt like it. Thanks very much. No sugar or milk, please, Sister, and very weak." I was surprised by her sudden laughter. "Whatever is the matter?"

"Here was I, imagining that I was going to put some flesh on you by drowning your tea with milk and sugar. Oh, dear! Oh, well, if you have it without, that is all there is to it."

When I had finished Nurse washed out the tumbler and tube, and put them on the locker. "Did you enjoy it?"

"Yes, it was lovely, and not only because it was my first cup."

"What else then?"

"Because Sister Linden made it for me."

"Really, June, you've got Sisteritis. You are as bad as Mr Casado."

"She's marvellous, nurse—and who, by the way, is Mr Casado? Sister seems particularly fond of him. All the time it's, 'Nurse, how is Mr Casado? We must take great care of him. Nurse, ask Mr Casado if he would care for some this or that.

I must pop across and see Mr Casado.' She's even telling me that I must meet this wonderful Mr Casado."

Nurse was laughing. "It sounds to me as if you might be a bit envious of Sister's affection for Mr Casado."

"Yes, I am. Very. Why does she fuss him so?"

"No one could help fussing over him. He really is quite wonderful. He's one of the students here, and he's very ill with a disease affecting both his kidneys, but he has always got a smile for everyone, and never a word of complaint. At the moment he's having a blood transfusion."

"Oh—I take it all back. But I don't think I'm exactly keen to meet him."

"You'll like him. Everybody does. And don't worry, he gets you rammed down his throat till he's sick of the sound of your name."

"How awful!"

"Yes, that's what he thinks. And now, are you going to lie there and think about Mr Casado's kidneys, or are you going to read?"

"Read, please, nurse. Page ninety-eight in the book with the black and red jacket."

She propped my book on my locker stand, then set it at the correct angle. "Call me when you want a page turned over."

"Yes, nurse, thank you—um, nurse?"

"Yes?"

"Look, don't let on, but I'm bursting to tell someone."

She laughed. "June, you are always bursting about something. What is it now?"

"Well, the physios and I think that one of my fingers is on the move. We're waiting until I can actually move it myself before we tell the doctors."

"Which one?"

"The middle one on my left hand. It moves when they put those electrical gadgets on it . . . so soon, nurse, I shall be able to turn pages for myself."

"That's grand, June, really grand. You'll find the others will come back quickly, now one has started."

"Will I, nurse? Just fancy, I'll be able to write to my parents.

Wonder if I can still write? I never thought anybody could get as excited over one solitary finger."

She smiled. "And I have no doubt Sister will be the first person you show it to."

Chapter 10

THINGS PLEASANT AND UNPLEASANT

I started to read but, finding it difficult to concentrate, gazed idly at what I could see. My vision was limited to the ceiling, and two of the beds on the opposite side of the ward: one to the left of the foot of mine, the other to the right. The patient in the bed on the left was a thin, peaky-faced woman with a duodenal ulcer. The bed on the right was surrounded by screens, and had been for three days, so I knew that the patient behind them must be extremely ill. I had not seen her but her marked foreign accent was sufficient indication that she was not English.

Staff Nurse came in view making her usual nightly round with aperients. She pushed her head over the screens at the foot of the foreigner's bed.

"Do you want an aperient, Mrs Manning?" Very English name, I thought.

"Aperient, nurse? What is that?" The reply came in an assuredly un-English voice.

Nurse chose a bottle of white, tacky, milk of magnesia from the trolley, then disappeared behind the screens with it.

"Oh—is it necessary that I have this thing?"

"No, you needn't if you don't want to, but you haven't had your bowels open for three days, and unless you can manage to do something about it, before tomorrow morning, you will have to have an enema."

"Enema, nurse? What is an enema?"

Nurse lowered her voice.

"I am sorry, nurse, but I do not still understand."

121

After considerable mumbling from Nurse I heard a sudden explosion of sound from the patient.

"Ah! Mein Gott, nurse! I know now what it is. I have had them much times before. It is that long, rubber thing that you poke, and poke, and poke, then fill with the soap bubbles. Mein Gott! Give me, please, the whole bottleful. I will drink it all."

Nurse proceeded to pour out a concoction guaranteed to purge, but not pleasantly.

When she reached my bed, she stopped, then came to peer into my face. "I thought so—you're bursting again, only this time it's with laughter. Why don't you read instead of listening to everything that goes on?"

I did try to read, but the more I thought about the soap bubbles, the more I laughed, until I felt a sudden, inexplicable cleavage inside me. That was no laughing matter. "Nurse!"

Staff Nurse hurried to my bedside at the urgency in my voice.

"Nurse, I'm breaking up inside. I've just had a horrid sensation—as if I'd split."

"Any pain?"

"No, not really, just a sort of tearing feeling."

She whisked away, to return with Sister and Dr Black. He bent over me: "Where did you feel this, June?"

"In my right side, doctor, just below my ribs."

He uncovered me, then dug the tips of his fingers into my side. "Here?"

"Yes, you're right on it."

"Did it last long?"

"No, it was quick and sharp. It went across my body, in a line, from side to centre."

"Feel anything now?"

"No."

He looked at Sister, who was taking my pulse. "It's jumping a bit, but that's not unusual for her." She turned to me. "What were you doing when it happened?"

"I was laughing."

Dr Black chewed the inside of his cheek. "Well, it sounds to me, Sister, as if she'd, literally, split her side laughing. All I can think of is that those muscle fibres had become adhered from disuse and the action caused by her laughter produced the sudden tearing, which was merely the fibres separating themselves again.''

That made us all laugh, but it did not produce any further disintegration in my body.

Next morning the pieces of cotton-wool on the ends of sticks were replaced by handkerchiefs, because I found that I could push air through my nose with sufficient force to produce a blow. My physiotherapists were inclined to be sceptical about the theory of my "split side", but when they discovered what a really creditable nose blow I had, they revised their opinion.

"Well, it's your right side, anyway, and that's the worst side, so here's hoping. Let's start with your finger today, before you get tired."

They plugged in the battery, placed my left arm and hand on a towel, and began my treatment. They had not been working long when Sister and Dr Timms walked in.

"Oh." It was a long drawn, and disappointed monosyllable.

Dr Timms looked down with a smile. "What is that for, June?" Then he spotted my finger waggling about in response to the electric current. "My word, Sister, look at that!"

"I know, but I wanted to be able to control it myself before you knew it was moving at all."

"I suppose, in future, we are going to have to ask if it is convenient to pop in and see you?" He was laughing, but both he and Sister looked so pleased about the finger that I forgot my disappointment at their untimely entrance. "Now, show me how you can blow."

I demonstrated, then tried to cough for him, and to lift my head. But my body was taking its own leisurely course, and one thing at a time seemed to be its plan of recovery.

"These are for you to go on with, June." Sister put a pile of handkerchiefs beside me.

That little pile of linen squares was not allowed out of my sight all day, because they represented one more step on the road to physical normality. I could see, hear, feel, and smell; I could breathe, I could swallow, I could laugh, I could blow my nose, even if I was unable to hold the handkerchief; and almost, I could move a finger.

"You know what?" I said to my physios. "I'm beginning to think all this is worth being paralysed for."

One of them looked up. "Don't get too excited, old thing, because we think there is another finger moving."

"Which one?" I cried.

"The index." They moved the towel, with my hand on it palm uppermost, onto the top of my chest where I could see it. As the current shot down my arm there was a faint flutter in my first finger, and quite a perceptible movement from my middle one.

"Can you take more current?"

"Yes, yes. Give them the works properly."

A hard core of pain, and my middle finger shot skywards, while my first one made a considerably weaker, but decided move in the same direction.

"Heck!" I said. "Give them some more."

The electrical treatment that the physiotherapists gave me was used to stimulate my muscles into activity, and to ensure their tone. They used two metal discs—working on an anodal and cathodal principle—one of which was placed somewhere on my spine, in this case behind my neck, the other being on a wooden handle, attached to which was a thin strip of metal called an interrupter. By the simple expedient of pressing the interrupter onto the disc, the current of electricity could be cut off, and when it was released, so was the current.

The strength of the current was controlled by an indicator on the top of the square box that housed the electrical mechanism, and from which ran the two leads to the two discs. Once my immunity to mild shock was established, I lost my fear of it and found it most fascinating, although it was, in theory, no more than a punctuated succession of shocks sent through the nerve track to the muscle, to activate the part of the body controlled by that muscle. A weak and sluggish muscle necessarily required a stronger current than a normal one, but its very sluggishness acted as a resistance against shock.

I awoke to hear beds being moved. The peaky-faced duodenal ulcer had gone and I could see a frighteningly white-faced woman propped up in the left-hand bed opposite. As she breathed she made a sound like metal being tipped out of a truck onto the road, and I found that I was unable to take my eyes off her. I was very glad when they put screens round her. When Nurse Sheldon came with my mail I asked her what was wrong with the white-faced patient.

"She's very ill."

"I know, nurse. She rattles all the time, and her mouth bleeds. Why?"

"Here, you read your mail and forget all about her."

Nurse held up a postcard of a Giotto fresco, from Italy. On the back were scrawled the words: "Everything produced here spirituoso—even the brunettes." She opened a letter from my father and held it for me to read. "Poor Puppa, he wants to know when he'll see my 'golden head', as he calls it, bobbing about in the river again." There was a food parcel from the local grocer, and a book token from the girls of my old school.

"Thank you, nurse. That was quite a haul."

"Yes, you're spoilt . . . what about some stout?"

"Yes, nurse, I'll have it before the physios come, please."

In between gulps I told her how itchy I was where the rim of plaster encircled my seat. "I'll go silly if it doesn't ease, nurse."

"I know. You're in for an itchy time, I'm afraid, but I'll relieve it temporarily for you."

She cut some small squares of lint, soaked them in calamine lotion, then slipped them up through the hole in Jimmy's back between the two of us. It was heaven; until the physios came, and I foolishly told them what kind Nurse Sheldon had done.

"Why do you think Mr Muir put you in this cast?"

"To keep me straight."

"Yes, and it's no use if you are going to have lumps of lint stuffed about inside the cast—it will alter your position." Nine pieces of calamine-cooled lint were pulled out from under me, while I wondered if such a thin piece of material could really throw me out of plumb.

"I think I'd like to blow my nose, please."

"Oh, no, you don't. You are going to have your breathing exercises first."

One girl clapped her hands round my ribs while the other amassed the paraphernalia required for my electrical treatment. I worked under direction, pulling what respiratory muscles I had in or out, up or down, or sideways; and I kept up a constant stream of hiccoughs and burps until we all subsided with giggles.

"Sorry, hic, it's the stout."

"Have you just had it?"

"Yes—oops! Pardon."

"Well you'd better choose another time, in future . . . one thing, there's plenty to go on with until you've stopped."

There certainly was plenty to go on with. I had two physio-therapists spending four to five hours on my inert body, every day except Sunday. Apart from breathing exercises and electrical treatment, there was massage to be done, and all my limbs to be put through their full range of passive movements twice a day. This entailed bending every joint in every toe and every finger separately, then doing the movements together; it meant that my feet were pulled upwards, downwards, sideways, and rotated from the ankle, as were my hands from the wrist; and it involved all the bigger movements from knees, hips, elbows, and shoulders. The physios lifted my heavy, unmanageable limbs about because I had to be kept supple, but was unable to participate actively. It saved my tendons and muscles from tightening and becoming short, for if they had been left to do so, when mobility returned it would have been of little value.

I did not mind this at all because it helped me to re-establish the pattern of the various movements in my mind, for I had lost all conception of what it even felt like to bend my limbs in certain directions. "Try to lift your head, try to move your toes, try to raise your arms, try to contract your seat muscles, try to arch your back. Never stop trying . . . try, try, try."

Stupid little word, I thought. There were times when my "triers" tried my patience, because the effort was so exhausting mentally. It was tedious beyond words while there was no visible result from this abortive trying, but now that something was happening to my fingers I could see the reason for it, and required no further admonition.

What I did require was help in training my mind to think of things that had previously needed no thought, because they were automatic.

"I hope my brain box doesn't burst before my body recovers."

"We'll give it a spell now, until after you've had lunch."

"What is that ghastly noise?"

"A patient across the way, breathing."

"Isn't it horrible?"

"Yes."

A few minutes later Nurse Sheldon was standing by my bed with my lunch, which was really midday dinner, but in hospital any meal eaten in the middle of the day seemed to be called lunch. We had breakfast at 8.30 a.m., when the day staff came on duty; what they called "elevenses", but which was morning tea to me, at 10.30 a.m.; lunch, which was dinner to me, at 12.30 p.m.; tea, which was afternoon tea to me, at 4 p.m.; and supper, which was tea to me because there was always soup and a savoury of sorts, at 7 p.m.

Nurse Sheldon tapped a fork against my teeth. "Come on, dreamy."

"Sorry, nurse."

"Look, would you like me to put some screens round you, when you've finished eating? You may get some sleep before your physios come."

"Yes, thanks, nurse."

One of the white-veiled figures woke me with apologies, but I did not mind, and soon forgot, because I moved my middle finger by myself for the first time. That night I dreamt I was swimming the river at home, with an effortless, stylish stroke: a graceful, moving body in a flowing volume of blue-green sea water. I awoke to the clank of bedpans, wash-basins, and the general hubbub of the morning round. I was firmly encased in Jimmy.

In a navy uniform with a white starched apron, the apologetic white poke bonnet that all the Sisters wore on her neatly-curled hair, Sister Linden came in through the bottom door of the ward. Those bonnets always made me want to laugh, they were such absurd things to sit on the heads of people who had to organize and control large hospital wards, because the lightning judgements that had to be made under their white starched frilliness were often ones concerning life or death. As Sister came in that morning, her head-piece looking rather like an outspread fan standing up on a little island of frills, I thought that its incongruity served only to emphasize the dynamic personality of this woman. She ruled us all, nurses, patients, and even doctors, with decisiveness and clarity of thought. That made her a person whom her patients and staff could trust, and on whom her superiors could rely. But it was not all that made Sister Linden what she was, for she ruled with an affection that was evident in her merry brown eyes and in her understanding and sympathetic heart. That made her a person whom we could all love.

She went to her desk, removed her cloak, sat down and took the report from Staff Nurse, who stood, decorously, and a little behind her right shoulder. Then she was at my bedside enquiring after my welfare.

"I am fine, thank you, Sister. Most uninteresting apart from a few itches."

"Yes, we'll have to do something about this itchiness of yours. Where does it worry you most?"

"Seat, heels, and shoulder-blades."

She turned back the bedclothes at the foot of the frame to expose Jimmy's clean whiteness and my two feet, nestling in an upright position, in his plaster embrace. She took one foot gently on either side of the instep.

"If you want to take it out, Sister, you will have to grab it by the big toe and pull."

"But surely there's some other way? Doesn't that hurt?"

"No, not a scrap. Same principle as a cat carrying her kittens by the scruff of the neck, I suppose. It's how the physios do it, anyway, and honestly, it doesn't hurt."

She looked as if she was leading someone to the guillotine, but she got it out, then held it aloft while she bent under it to examine my heel. "When did you get these blisters?"

"Didn't know I had them. My heels burn a bit, that's all."

"Are they rubbed?"

"Yes, by both nurses and physios."

She replaced my leg gingerly. "I shall have to find out about it—meantime we'll put in a small pressure ring. . . . Nurse ——"

A small, frightened-looking probationer came hurrying.

"Nurse, make two small pressure rings to put in the heels of June's cast—and give them a good rub. Do her seat too."

"Yes, Sister."

"And hurry, nurse."

A timid, "Yes, Sister."

Nurse put screens round my bed then spread an assortment of cotton-wool, gauze, methylated spirits, and tears, on my locker.

"Hey! Whatever's up? Don't you want to do it?"

"No, I want to do it—sniff—but it's Sister." Her tears were flowing faster.

"Look, you blow your nose and tell me what is wrong with Sister. You're lucky to be on her ward."

"Yes, I know. They say you learn an awful lot here, and I want to be with her, but I'm so slow, and she's always at me to hurry up—especially when I'm doing beep rounds."

She's picking up the jargon quickly, I thought, because some new nurses were ages on the ward before they passed through the bedpan stage, to B.P.s, and finally beeps. "Well, you can clap on pace when you're doing beeps easily enough."

"But I can't, that's just the trouble. There always seems to be so many people about, and I've got to stand aside and wait for them because they're all my seniors."

"But, nurse, when you've got a beep or two in your hand you've got the right of way—you know, like the man with the biggest truck in heavy traffic. Don't you give a fig for anyone.

I've seen students divert their course at times because of a nurse with her eye on the sluice room only. You go as fast as professional dignity will allow—really charge—and you'll find you will be left a clear field."

She giggled. "I think I'll try."

"Don't think, nurse. You do it, and don't hang about while patients decide whether they want a beep or not. Just give it to them. Beeps have a sort of mass effect on bladders—you'll get results. And if Sister tells you to hurry, don't shrink into your uniform like a crab into its shell, you look her straight in the eye, and say 'Yes, Sister' in a firm voice that lets her know you mean it—and go for it. She is a very direct person herself, and she likes her nurses to show a little initiative, and get about the ward with purpose in their walk and bearing. You watch her too. If there is any shinannicking from any patient, Sister is the first one there. She goes straight to the source of any trouble. All she says is 'Now what's all this about?' and things seem to fall into place again. Don't be frightened of her. Stiffen your backbone, like she does when there's a flap on, and get the most important job done first . . . and now I've finished, you have a chocolate while you finish making those. The box is inside my locker, I think."

She made a very neat job of the rings, and my heels stopped burning as they lay suspended in the centre of them, relieved from all pressure. Before Nurse had time to remove the screens my physios had descended upon us.

"One of Mr Muir's assistants is coming up to look at your heels and back, June."

"How did he know?"

"Sister has just rung the orthopaedic department."

I looked at the little pro who was gathering up her débris. She smiled and nodded: "I see what you mean. No dilly-dallying."

The physios had not been working long when a doctor with a shock of black hair and a blue chin appeared. He took my feet out of the cast, removed the carefully made rings, replaced my feet, then pressed on them with his hands.

"Burn?"

"Yes."

"Mm . . ." He let his hands dangle in the pockets of his white coat, as if he were resting them. "I don't like these clawed toes either. I'll try some Stam soles. What size shoes do you take?"

"Sevens." He was gone quickly.

"Who is that doctor?"

"That's Mr Pastaad-Noyes, one of the orthopaedic surgeons. He is Mr Muir's right-hand man . . . now, you do some breathing exercises, because if we've got to do any plaster work for him, we'll not have a chance to get through."

But Mr Noyes was back in a few minutes with two thin leather soles, that looked exactly like the soles of Roman sandals, except for five steel spikes, about two inches long, protruding from the toe of each. He proceeded to remove my feet, and the rings; then slid one sole against the inside of the shell, and flush against Jimmy's plaster foot. The leather soles were wider than Jimmy's, and he refused to budge, so the two physios were ordered to attack one foot while Mr Noyes took the other. They hacked, cut, and chipped, with files and shears, scattering scales of plaster everywhere. Jimmy proved obstinate, but at last they managed to carve out a groove sufficiently wide to accommodate the Stam soles, which were given a final pat in position before my feet were carefully replaced. They sat up jauntily against the leather, leaving a comical array of spikes silhouetted against the cream wall opposite.

The doctor produced a long piece of black tape from his pocket, cut it into lengths, then to our complete amazement he flattened one big toe against one spike and tied it in position with one of the lengths of tape, topping everything with a neat little flat bow over the joint. "Ah . . ." He stood back with an air of satisfied approval. He put some of the tapes on my other foot, and looked at the physios. "You tie up the others, please. I'll attend to this foot."

Ten nice straight toes, ten neat little black bows, ten spikes sticking up above those toes and bows like church-spires.

I got the giggles properly: then my giggles changed to choking laughter.

Mr Noyes stood viewing my feet with pride, and a reluctant smile; the physios struggled with silent laughter; Dr Black, Sister and I were quite unrestrained until I began to choke. Sister hastened away for a glass of water, the physios pushed my ribs in and out, while Mr Noyes stood by telling me when to draw breath and when to release it. I was surprised at this disruption in my breathing because I imagined that it was strong enough to withstand any violence, but it settled down after some coaxing and Mr Noyes resumed his examination of my itchiness. He decided that I must be taken out of Jimmy so that he could take a detailed report of my back to Mr Muir.

Taking me out of Jimmy was no mean task as it required eight people; four to take care of my four separate limbs; one to act as my neck, to stop my head from flopping about; and three to lift the carcass. It was necessary also that these eight people move at one time, and as one body. Mr Noyes made me a splendid backbone with his arm, holding my googly head firm against his chest with his free hand. That was all that worried me. I did not mind particularly what happened to my limbs, but I was loth to lose my head.

The major difficulty was what to do with me when they had me in their arms, because four of the weight-lifters were separated from the other four by an iron bed, and as they could not go on holding me while they argued about it, more helpers were called to remove Jimmy and his frame and put a mattress on the planks. All this had to be done by a kind of burrowing process through a tunnel, of which I was the roof, my eight upholders the two sides, and the bed the bottom. Eventually, I was lowered onto the mattress while arms were flexed and Mr Noyes examined my back.

All too soon I was ready to be put back, a task requiring a greater degree of skill than my exhumation. There was only one way I could be fitted into my shell and that did not include an array of arms, which did not belong to me, but which had to clutch me until the last possible moment. I was the only one who enjoyed the procedure because I was the only one who did not, and could not, literally, have a hand in it somewhere. Out of a total of eighty digits I think only three were damaged sufficiently to admit pain, but they all belonged to different people who were heroically uncomplaining.

"What have you done to Jimmy?" I cried as soon as I felt him close about me again.

"Don't you feel straight, June?"

"Yes, but he feels so smooth and nice. He even smells sweet."

Sister stood straightening her apron and belt. "Nurse brushed him out for you, and sprinkled some talcum powder in him while she had the chance. Does it really make such a difference?"

"Oh, yes, Sister, it's lovely. He must have been full of bits and pieces."

She smiled. "He certainly was."

Mr Noyes looked up from the foot of the bed. "Have her toes tied up at night only, Sister. They'll have to be free in the day for exercising."

"Very well."

He had gone.

I tried to sleep but always, as I dozed off, I became conscious of the rattling breathing of the patient across the way and sleep fled, because I worried about her. From the other bed opposite, and on my right, there emerged, now that the screens were down, the face of the foreigner: smooth wide brow, long curving eyebrows, shapely lids over eyes widely spaced and grey, a fine straight nose, beautifully moulded mouth, and a chin that completed the perfect contours of her oval face. Her hair was dark brown, braided in two long shining plaits.

"What nationality is she?" I asked Nurse Sheldon as she gave me my lunch.

"Hungarian."

"But she's got an English name."

"Yes, she married some Englishman during the war. She's got a little boy. He's left her—the husband, I mean."

"The rotter! Fancy leaving a sick woman with a child—and she's so beautiful."

Nurse shrugged. "She's a wonderful patient too—I don't see why, myself, and the worst of it is he can't even support her. He just seems to vanish, and when they find him he has no money for maintenance so they put him in prison."

"Fat lot of good that does her."

"Exactly."

"Nurse, could I give her one of my food parcels?"

"She's terribly proud, my dear. I don't think she would accept it. You'll have to think of something less obvious."

I thought very hard about it until Nurse called me to boot for not attending to the business of swallowing my lunch. That disposed of, my physios were upon me again and while they exercised the immobilized parts of me I concentrated on exercising the two fingers of my left hand. We were all silent but intent.

"Ah!" I said. "Enter the big man."

They both looked up astonished.

"Mr Muir. He's just come in. I can hear him talking to Sister."

"Really, June . . ."

"And he has a presence," I said.

"Who has a presence?" Sister queried. The physios looked fearful.

"Anthony Eden. Good morning, Mr Muir."

"Good morning—we're going to make you another cast, to go on top of you, and follow the contours of your body fairly accurately."

I could not question his motives but I did not see the sense in encasing the top of me in plaster because Jimmy held my head, back, hips, and legs firmly in position.

I had a long exhaustive afternoon's treatment, which was carried on through tea-time without a break. It was after five when Nurse Sheldon brought me my tea.

"What a day you've had," she said. "But you're lucky. The others have had their tea long ago, so Sister asked Mrs Venning to make you some cheese on toast. I could eat it myself."

"May I have a drink first, please, nurse?"

"Yes, of course." She stood by my bed, holding the glass tube in position in the tumbler of tea. I always had my drinks out of a glass tumbler because it was easier for them to see when they had to tilt it for me as I neared the bottom. I finished my drink and had eaten a few mouthfuls of toast when I became aware of a sudden stillness in the ward.

"Funny, Nurse—everything's gone quiet."

"Has it?"

Then I realized what it was. Just as the loud ticking of a clock that one has become accustomed to causes a surprised silence when it stops, so had the cessation of the rattles opposite.

"It's the patient opposite, Nurse. I'd got quite used to her noisy breathing. Does that mean she's better?"

"Yes—come on, eat up." My usually smiling Nurse Sheldon spoke sharply, for her. My mind leapt at horror.

"Nurse," I whispered, "she's just died, hasn't she? That's why there is no more noise."

Nurse looked down at me. "Oh, well, you'll have to know sooner or later. . . . Yes, I'm afraid she has."

"But, nurse, she is young, and she has two little girls."

"I know, I know, but they've done everything within their power to save her—for goodness' sake, don't take it to heart so. Here, have some more toast."

But my attempts to eat were futile because it was impossible not to think of the dead woman opposite me, and the thought of her made me choke. Nurse retreated uncomplainingly with my partially consumed tea. She had only been gone a few moments when Sister Linden appeared at my bedside. I thought she had come to chide so I spoke up quickly, but quietly:

"I'm sorry about my tea, Sister, but I couldn't eat, really I couldn't, while I knew there was a dead person just over there."

Sister put a soft hand on mine. "You needn't apologize, my dear. I only came to ask you if you would like to be taken out of the ward for a while—onto the balcony."

"Oh, Sister, I'd love that. Could you manage it?"

"Yes, we'll get some porters, and the students will help. We shall lift you, and Jimmy, and the frame, onto a trolley as you are. Cheer up—there's a good girl."

They wheeled me away from death down a long corridor,

past a lift, the hospital chapel and the gynaecological ward, through some big glass doors, and into the glory of an English August evening. Against a blue-washed sky, streaked with white clouds, gulls wheeled, calling their plaintive cry that carried me back to the Thames Pool, the sea, and freedom.

"Sister?"

But Sister had gone; so had the porters and the students. I was left with the graceful gulls, banking cleanly against the ever-changing backcloth of sky and cloud; and a black arrow-head of starlings as they twittered homewards. The leaves of a tall plane tree, beyond the balcony, flickered idly, green blotches letting in a patch of blue where they would; from a small window across a street a knotted hand tossed bread to pigeons. And I started to sing: very quietly, at first, but as I looked from the sky, to birds, to tree, and back to sky again, I opened my mouth, laughed aloud, and let a song of the sea rip out into the startled air. It was the first time I had sung for over four months. I only stopped my bellowing because I was afraid it might lead to breathing trouble.

"Well—that was quite a recital!" It was a quiet voice, full of laughter, coming from the right of me.

My eyes swivelled quickly in anger. A stinging retort was checked on my lips as I saw the smile on the face of the speaker. I was sure, from the look in those eyes, that anything I had to say would bring forth a quip that would, in all probability, be unanswerable.

"Pardon the intrusion, but I was sent by Sister Linden to see if you were all in one piece. It is obvious that you are. You sound on top of the world, difficult, I should imagine, for one who by nature and nurture belongs to the bottom of it."

"Have you ever been to New Zealand?"

"No, this is my first contact with it in any shape or form."

"I certainly do it no credit, but even if you people consider it the bottom of the world, it is not the end."

"I'll reserve my judgement . . . and seriously, is there anything you want from the ward?"

"If you're going back you might ask Sister if I may have a drink, please."

"I'll get you a drink myself."

He was gone with a long stride, quite at variance with his erect, well-built, but shortish figure. He wore a blue and brown paisley silk dressing-gown, so I assumed that he was a patient from the men's side of the ward. Black hair waved thickly over a splendidly shaped head, and his face was arresting with its mixture of impudence and nobility.

He was back promptly with a glass of orange juice.

"Where's Nurse?"

"I'll give it to you. I think I'm capable of holding a glass tube in a tumbler. But yell if I throttle you."

I was thirsty and drank greedily, soon draining the tumbler. "Thanks very much."

"Do they all guzzle like that in the Antipodes?"

"Look, how did you know I came from the Antipodes?"

"How did I know? How could I help knowing? I've had daily reports on you ever since you returned to Alexandra ward."

"Oh." I started to laugh. So did he. "It's tit for tat, then. You, I presume, are the much petted and fussed Mr Casado."

"Perez—to all and sundry. We should have exchanged hats sooner, you know, but I wasn't exactly dead nuts on meeting you." He cocked an amused eyebrow. "Seems it cut both ways."

"Yes, it did. Look, while you're here, perhaps you can tell me what Mr G. W. R. Paddington does. There's an enormous concrete building over there, several storeys high by what I can see of it, and it's got G.W.R. Paddington on it, so I presume——"

"But, Great Scott! Surely you know what that is? That's the Great Western Railway, Paddington. Didn't you know, honestly?" He sounded incredulous.

"How could I know? If you were in New Zealand and came across a sign saying 'Pohutu Geyser', would you know what it was?"

"No, I must admit I shouldn't. What is it?"

The night sky and the plane tree witnessed a cross chat of the city of London and the thermal areas of New Zealand. Two

OVER MY DEAD BODY

porters loomed in the doorway, with Nurse Sheldon, to propel me back to the ward. The duodenal ulcer was back in position opposite me and I had the beautiful Hungarian to contemplate. I was glad the empty bed had been moved elsewhere.

Sister came to ask me how I had enjoyed my break on the balcony.

"Sister Linden, were you born on the Sabbath?"

"What an extraordinary question! I don't know. Why?"

"Well, you know the old saying—'A child that's born on the Sabbath day, is wise, and kind, and——' "

"You do talk nonsense, June. Good night." She was laughing.

"Good night, Sister."

As she walked out of the big ward doors I wondered if she realized that I had only been trying to thank her for what she was doing for me.

Chapter 11

IN TRUTH I AM A MUMMY

————~~~~\\\\\\()\\\\\\~~~~————

Next morning Sister came straight to my bed after taking the report from Nurse. She held a rubber skull-cap in her hand.

"Have you had a really thorough wash, June?"

"Yes, Sister, I'm sure I'm shining. Is Mr Muir going to make the other cast today?"

"Yes. Help me fit this cap on June's head, please, nurse, then find a T bandage to wrap round her."

They tugged strenuously until the cap, with all my hair inside it, was smoothly tight against my head. Nurse tied what looked like a piece of white calico round my groin, and I was lifted in Jimmy, in the frame, onto a trolley from the operating theatre. In theatre the Sister came to inspect Jimmy, and to lay some cotton-wool and waterproof sheeting along his sides.

"Am I to stay in this cast, Sister, while the other one is being made?"

"Yes, they've got to fit each other, and you, exactly."

"Where do I fit?"

"Inside."

"But how do I breathe, and how do I get out?"

She laughed. "They will leave your face uncovered. Just how you get out, I do not know."

It was apparently an enigma to all of us except the big man. Sister bared my body. Jimmy, I thought, we're for it.

"I think we'd better put something over your chest. It won't be so embarrassing." She laid a flat piece of calico across me and under my arms, tucking it down tightly between Jimmy and me. Draped bodies were pushing their way into the theatre.

Mr Muir bent over me and plucked the centre of the strip of calico covering my chest between his index finger and his thumb.

"What is this for?"

Theatre Sister looked across my body at him. "I thought it would be less embarrassing for June."

He looked down quickly in astonishment: "You're not embarrassed, are you, June?"

I was, but I looked him straight in the eye: "No," I said, with a conviction I was far from feeling.

"Good. We want this cast to fit you, and it won't be much use if this is next to you. It will spoil its shape." His hand flicked upwards and the calico was tossed onto a chair. He looked round his five assistants.

"Ready?"

"Yes, sir."

The construction of this cast was neither the bother to the surgeons, nor the ordeal to me, that Jimmy had been, for I was appreciably stronger, my breathing was much improved, and I lay comfortably on my back while the operation was in progress. Fewer layers were applied, and the whole operation was disappointingly dull after the clamour heralding Jimmy's appearance.

I was contemplating the boredom of proceedings as I lay with the cold new cell on top of me, when Mr Muir turned aside quickly, then back again, and said:

"Shut your eyes, June."

I did so, only to open them immediately on feeling pressure from a long, slim, steely blade against my chin. "What are you doing?" I whispered.

"I'm not doing anything yet, but I am about to trim the neck of this cast. Please close your eyes."

The glimpse of that knife-like edge was sufficient. Fear, more than the command, closed my eyes before I thought, with comfort, of the knowledge and skill of this big man, whose only use for a knife was to save lives, not to destroy them. My throat, of course, could not even boast a scratch, and the now solidified cast was lifted from me. My body was a sickly yellow

green from the petroleum jelly and dotted with chips of con-
fetti-like plaster, which Theatre Sister was picking off me.

I returned to the ward and looked in some bewilderment at
my bed. "Things have been going on in our absence, Jimmy,"
I said aloud.

Fitted to all four corners of the bed were long wooden poles
standing perpendicularly, seven feet from the floor and approximately four feet, I guessed, above Jimmy and me, had we been
on our planks. At the head and foot of the bed these pairs of
poles were joined across by two short lengths. The latter were
notched at intervals of about three inches, and into corresponding sets of these notches were fitted two more long poles, running down the full length of the bed, and resting horizontally
above the planks. They were thus seven feet from the floor.

Sister was hastening towards us. "How are you, June?"

"Grand, thank you, Sister. Whatever is all that clobber over
my bed?"

"Oh, that—that's a Balkan beam."

"Looks like an Elizabethan four-poster, minus the draperies.
What's it for?"

"It's for your physios. Nurse, you will have to get every
piece of plaster off her, as well as all this jelly. I can't stay."

"Why is that called a Balkan beam, nurse?"

Nurse shrugged. "Search me. It's a beam named after a man
called Balkan—that's all I know."

"Did he invent it, or whatever?"

"I suppose so. What on earth were they doing up in theatre
to get you in such a mess? I'll never clean this off in a month
of Sundays."

Despite the fact that I was scrubbed three times that day,
Jimmy and I were not on friendly terms by evening. The
waterproofing had not prevented pieces of plaster slipping into
his inner lining, in consequence of which I spent a sleepless
itchy night, while Nurse spent profitless hours diving down
between us after elusive scraps of plaster. I had once read of
the Chinese poet Sung Tu Po, that he considered a man had
not proved himself to be of any great virtue in the forbearance
of pain—it was the discipline of mind required to resist the

urge to scratch, whenever he itched, that was the true test of manhood. I thought it rather an odd standard of judgement when I read it, but now I understood only too well.

"Nurse," I said, "in serving my term in Hell I expect I shall be encased in plaster from top to toe, and left to itch until my sins be remitted me."

"Yes, and I'll be put next to you, and made to scratch."

My anterior shell was still in the drying-room next morning when my physios arrived, trailing ropes, pullies, canvas slings, and innumerable springs.

"What in heaven's name are all those things for?"

"They're for your treatment. Mr Muir says it's time you started moving."

I failed to associate movement with all the apparatus that they now draped over my inert body, but the idea was a joy to contemplate. Piece by piece the struggling jumble was attached to the two horizontal bars of the Balkan beam until a network of slings, springs, and ropes, swung above me. The physios climbed on the planks, on chairs, on the frame, on Jimmy, but not on me. For that I was grateful. Although they worked rapidly it was well on in the morning before the last knot was tied, the last spring attached, and the last sling hooked into position.

"You know," I said, while they were doing my passive movements, "I don't want to worry you, but what——"

"Yes, we know . . . what is all this for?" The girl called Nita looked up and smiled.

While they bent over my body they told me the story of the conglomeration hanging over their heads. . . .

An enterprising physiotherapist, in the days when little was known of the profession, and equipment for it was negligible, conceived the idea of making use of "slings and springs" for cripples. She was out sailing with her husband and marvelled at the ease with which a spinnaker billowed at a touch, sails were reefed or unfurled, all by a system of cleats, ropes, pulleys and knots. It looked simple enough, so why couldn't she apply it in her work? What was to stop patients being hoisted aloft to sail in air? She experimented with canvas slings, setting the

inert limb in the sling, then hauling it up into the air by means of a cleat and two ropes attached to a Balkan beam. Later, springs were added to give more resiliency, and greater range of movement, to weakened muscles. It took years to establish her theory as a practical contribution in the treatment of the disabled. Tradition dies hard, and here was a mere woman attempting to apply her rudimentary knowledge of yachting to paralysed limbs. But it worked. She saw to it that it did, and was rewarded by the growing demand for "slings and springs" in every physiotherapy department in every hospital.

My physios, who referred to this process of suspension as "slinging up", and worked on while the coast was clear, drew screens round me, and began to sling my legs. They slipped a canvas sling under each knee, then hooked the slings to springs, which were attached to ropes hanging from the beam. On each foot they put a thing they called a "toggle", a long piece of canvas which they twisted round my foot in a figure eight so that my heel was hanging through the bottom loop, and a hook attached to a spring through the two iron rings of the top loop. They stood, one on either side of the bed, with one hand on the cleat of the rope leading from the sling under my knee, and the other on the cleat of the rope from the toggle.

"Right?" The dark girl looked across at the one called Nita.

Four hands pulled four cleats downwards; the slings, the springs, and my two legs shot upwards; the cleats were fixed, leaving my legs suspended in the air. It was wonderful. Nita gave my right leg a push with her hand. It lunged across space to bump the other one into activity and they both started swinging.

"Heck! That's marvellous." I laughed. "Can't you push them any harder?"

Nita looked at her companion, who was smiling. "Very well —let her play, today. We'll really get down to business tomorrow."

As soon as my legs slowed down, Nita would set them off again. They swung high and low, to one side then the other, and I silently blessed the lady who had invented the slings and springs for the freedom that they brought.

The physios worked tirelessly. I marvelled at their patience, for their task was as monotonous as it was laborious, yet they managed to bring joy and laughter to their work, and me to a pitch of enthusiasm for which they would take no due credit. We battled, not only against an unresponsive body, but also against fatigue, for despite the stout, which I was imbibing every evening, and the consequent increase in my general well-being, it took very little to tire me. I was prone to fall asleep, even with a ward full of bustle and noise, and on the day of my first "slinging up" I slept as soon as the physios left me.

Nurse Sheldon woke me at half-past five. "Come on, Dopey-Opie, you'll be having your tea, and your wash, and your supper, all in one soon. Sister's out in the kitchen making you a cup of tea."

"Sister is a brick."

I was halfway through tea when a porter walked through the big doors carrying something huge and white. "Where do you want this, nurse?"

Nurse Sheldon turned abruptly. "Oh! I say—against the wall, I think, on the other side of the bed."

He stood his burden against the wall, gave it an affectionate pat, grinned at nothing in particular, and went.

Jimmy's better half had arrived. At the top was a neat curve that would fit under my chin, and at the bottom two smaller curves that would fit over my feet where the toes joined. There was not the least doubt that she had been fashioned to my contours: she was altogether too fashionable.

"Please, nurse, put it under the bed out of sight."

Nurse picked her up tenderly, giving me a wicked look. "It's a shame."

"It's the most shameless thing I've seen in years."

"No, I mean, to hide it. All right, all right! I'm putting it away."

Her exit was followed by the appearance of Dr Hume and Perez Casado, who pulled up abruptly at the sight of my four-poster and my awnings.

"What's it all in aid of?" Dr Hume was marching round the bed.

"It's for slinging me about."

They examined the tackle and talked idly until Perez Casado came just a little too near the bed, and stubbed his slippered toe. He kicked; something moved; and he bent down mystified.

"What on earth have you got under your bed?"

He emitted a long whistle. "I say, Basil, come and look at this."

Dr Hume hastened round from the other side of the bed. His green eyes sparkled.

"Well! Talk about a curvaceous cast!" He stood it up in front of him. "My word, she's a beauty. You mustn't keep her under the bed, June—it's not right. Let's leave her standing." He propped her up alongside my bed, stood back, and they both continued to admire her. Dr Hume was smiling, twirling his stethoscope, and eyeing the cast. "Who made it?"

"Mr Muir."

Perez Casado looked at me with a grin. "After all, one can't blame Mr Muir for its irregularities."

Dr Hume shouted with laughter. "He was handicapped by the shape under the cast."

They walked away before I could think of a retort.

I was just going to call Nurse to dispose of the body, when Dr Meiklejohn appeared, with a book he had promised to bring me. "Sorry to be—phew! What have we here?" His eyes were on the cast, then they roamed over the beam, the trappings, and finally, back to the cast. He picked it up, examined it thoroughly, then, as Nurse Sheldon came towards me with a wash-basin, he started unbuttoning his white coat.

Nurse Sheldon looked her surprise. "Will you be needing June?"

"No, no, nurse——" He picked up Jimmy's better half, tucked it under his chin, flattened it against his chest, buttoned his white coat round her smooth curves, and took a few shuffling steps up and down the ward.

Poor Nurse Sheldon shed all dignity, and I was no better.

"Please, please, Doctor Meiklejohn, take it off!"

He had to go because Nurse wanted to wash me. She put the

much-abused shell under the bed once more. She did not come out until next morning, when the man came to sweep under my bed. He stood the cast against the wall, eyeing it the while questioningly, and with awe. The first students began to dribble in. Their startled looks gave way to ones of interest and admiration. They examined her, fitted her on themselves, and were considerate enough to hide her indecencies under the bed when they had finished with her. But the word had spread, and amidst laughter, but more surreptitiously than the students, the nurses squeezed themselves into her curves. It was neither my fault, nor the big man's, that she would not fit everyone.

I still did not know for what purpose she was intended, but with the arrival of my physios I begged to become acquainted with it. I was screened off, my bedclothes, and gown removed, then the shell was laid over me. There was nothing to be seen of me except my face and the tips of my toes from which the bows had been untied. They could do anything with me in this, I thought, except sit me on a chair. I wondered what I should look like in an Egyptian tomb. Canvas slings were threaded between Jimmy and the frame: one under his shoulders; the other under his knees. Ropes hanging from the beam were hooked to the slings. With a physio attending each one of the four ropes I was hoisted from the frame, the cleats were fixed, and I was swinging in mid-air, entirely encompassed in plaster.

The frame was removed to allow a mattress to be thrown on to the planking, on which the frame rested. Two long, canvas straps, about two inches in width, were strapped right round us—the two casts and myself. Still suspended from the beam I was revelling in the swing as the heavy weight of the plaster plus dead body rocked back and forth. Then I heard the voice of one of my physios.

"Are you ready, June?"

I had no idea what I was supposed to be ready for. "Yes."

"Right. One-two—THREE!"

On the word "three" I was unexpectedly flipped over to find myself lying face downwards, my body weight now being transferred to the new cast. I was still swinging, but that was the neatest piece of manœuvring I had ever witnessed. They had only tossed me once. With Jimmy covering my back, legs, and head, there was very little I could see and nothing I could do.

"All right?" came a query from above me.

"Yes, I'm fine."

I was slowly lowered to the mattress, the ropes released, and Jimmy lifted from my back.

"Quick—turn her head to one side."

"Thanks," I said as I drew breath again, for Jimmy had pushed my head into the mattress with such vigour as to stop up my nostrils, and my mouth. My spine maintained its correct position by the support from the cast in which I now rested. The new shell was comfortable, the relief of Jimmy's clutches unbelievable, and the reversal of my habitual position an unimagined joy.

"Just look at her back."

I was indignant. "What's the matter with it?"

"The stuff that's stuck to it! No wonder you itched. There's chips of plaster, crumbs, hairs, even an orange pip, masses of dry skin, and as for this ring round your bottom—we had better get a nurse, and gallons of water."

The scrubbing brush was a delight. Without the friction of clothes or movement my body was covered with a scale of dead skin which, if it did fall off, only fell into Jimmy.

I clenched my teeth, squirmed inwardly with delight, and cried for more.

"Harder, nurse, harder—over to the right—no, back this way a little—ah! That's lovely. Now down. Between my shoulder-blades, please, nurse, and harder—a little more to the left. Hard please. Scrub hard."

Nurse paused to draw breath. She pushed a red and perspiring face close to mine. "This is worse than polishing my father's car, and goodness knows he's fussy enough."

Jimmy and I could not recognize each other that evening. With my smooth skin, well-sprinkled and creamed, and his powdered interior, life seemed too sweet. I would have walked halfway round the world over broken bottles for the big man that night.

147

Chapter 12

MY ENGLISH HOME

———~wwwww(O)wwww———

Next morning I could hold a pencil between my trembling fingers, and my handkerchief to my nose. Someone had to move my hand about for me but that did not detract, in any way, from my excitement, because I had begun writing my first letter to my parents. With a pillow on my chest, a book propped against it, a sheet of paper tethered to the book, and my left hand sand-bagged in position, I weaved a spidery pattern of words. In three days I had covered seven pages, comprising a total of fifteen short sentences. Excitement, paralysis, fatigue, and the fact that I was an extremely right-handed person by nature, resulted in a broken conglomeration of letters that were large, badly formed, and shaky. Perez Casado put it in an envelope and addressed it for me.

"I wonder if it will take your mother and father as long to read this as you took to write it."

"I shall be amazed if they can read it at all . . . never mind, come what may, it's a beginning. I'll probably be able to write with both hands by the time the month is out."

That was the first day in September, and I was to learn that this disease of mine was one from which I was not going to make a sudden, or spectacular, recovery. Jimmy, it appeared, was to be a permanency for some considerable time and, as I had already tried to tell Dr Hume, his job, being honourable, made his name honourable, so the least I could do was to pay him homage.

One night during the second week in September screens were put round me, a group of students whom I had befriended, Dr Meiklejohn, Dr Black, Perez, and a night nurse, arrayed themselves inside the screens. The beds on either side of me were unoccupied and we had decided to hold an early ceremony before patients were asleep. Perez, who had helped himself to a little pure alcohol from the dispensary, stood at Jimmy's head, visible in the filtering circle of light from my shaded bed lamp. He bowed low and chanted:

> "Oh, Jimmy, thou being of ignoble design;
> Unacknowledged saviour of this young girl's spine,
> We hereby acclaim—
> With drink to sustain—
> The prolongation of your inimitable line."

The alcohol dripped on Jimmy's head and, the ceremonial rites thus completed, two of the students carefully drew his better half from under the bed. She was lying stomach-down on the floor as her inside contained our supper. We feasted well on the contents of her interior, which brought forth an assortment of fruit cake, biscuits, sweets, meat, and fruit; all in tins, and all from New Zealand.

Sister Linden, on her usual round of the patients next morning, registered a little bewilderment as she stood talking to me. She walked away towards the next bed, paused, then came back. Her nose twitched as she said apologetically, and hesitantly:

"June, you—er—haven't been drinking, have you?"

"No," I replied decisively, "I have not."

Sister walked away again, satisfied that I had not, but still puzzled. The next time she was out of the ward I hastily summoned a nurse and asked her to tip as much perfume as she could onto Jimmy's head, without drenching the plaster. It was no sooner done than Dr Hume swung into view.

"Good morning." He sniffed, not very appreciatively, so I concluded that it must have been a cheap bottle of scent. "Jimmy developed into a perfume merchant?"

"Sort of, I suppose. They've—um—been putting some smelly stuff on my hair."

"Must have laid it on with a shovel. You reek to high heaven. How do they manœuvre your head to get at your hair?"

"You see those two things, like pieces of tow, sticking out just above my hair line?"

"Horns—yes."

"Plaits, Doctor Hume. Well, they grab those to lever my head out of Jimmy, and while one nurse supports my head on the right side, the other nurse brushes, combs, and replaits the left—then vice versa. Actually, it's very simple and quick."

"June, can you lift your head yet?"

I shut my eyes, clenched my teeth, and endeavoured to set some machinery going inside my brain that would make my neck take the weight of my head. But there was nothing except a grunt of unrewarded effort. I opened my eyes. "I tried."

"You don't need to tell me."

"Why? Did you see something move?"

"No. But you look just like a choking chicken." He looked up as a crisp step sounded in the ward. "Good morning, Doctor Timms."

"Good morning, Hume. Well, June?"

"Can I lift my head? You ask Doctor Hume this time, not me."

Dr Timms turned with a laugh.

"No, she can't. I have just witnessed an attempt."

The keen eyes shifted back to me. "Tired of trying?"

"No, I'm not, because it's only beginning to get interesting, but my biggest trouble at the moment is to know what to concentrate on most."

"At the moment, in raising your head off that plaster."

"Why is that so important, Doctor Timms?"

"If you can't support your head, you won't be able to sit up, even when your back recovers. Your head would loll about like a new-born baby's. The only way you could sit up would be with a big steel collar round you. And there is nothing I can do about it except to say, keep at it."

So I kept at it. In the past I had often been hot from physical exertion; but I now realized that it was possible to sweat under mental labour. Things fairly buzzed inside my head until the heat was too much, little popping noises came to my ears, and stars to my eyes: then I gave up. Night time was the best for

thought, because the ward was quiet, and darkness shut me
off from other distractions. I wondered if they had any sus-
picions as to why I snatched every available opportunity to
close my eyes during the day time. But my days were busy,
there were too few opportunities when I was left alone. The
first of the day staff came on duty at 8.30 a.m. and their arri l
was the forerunner of an unceasing round of activity.

Our ward contained thirty-two beds in all, sixteen on the
men's side and sixteen on the women's, these two sides being
separated by the main corridor on the first floor of the hospital. We had three more storeys on top of us, the outpatients'
department, then the kitchen, in basement layers beneath the
ground floor. There was even a swimming-pool in the basement under the medical school, and a network of overhead,
and underground, tunnels connecting the nurses' home to
main hospital, medical school to main hospital, private wing
to main hospital, and ward to ward. The operating theatres
were all on the top floor, casualty and the orthopaedic ward
on the ground floor.

Mine was a teaching ward for physicians and, therefore, contained medical patients whose chests, hearts, stomachs, and
entrails, offered an ever-varying reaction to offensive bugs—or
bacilli as I had heard them called. I occupied a bed in this ward
by the kind permission, but not the wholehearted approval, of
the physician in charge. At first he did not even glance my way
as he passed up the ward. Then he began to acknowledge me
with a shrug of resignation. Finally he smiled his apparent
acceptance of me. I never knew what he thought inwardly
because I had stolen a bed from him, and my inclusion in the
ward meant one ulcer, one chest, or one spleen, less for him to
demonstrate before his students. I was a nuisance in Alexandra
ward: a nuisance to the physician, to Mr Muir, and to Dr
Timms, because I was not in the right place. But not once did
I acquiesce to being transferred to another ward, nor did they
carry it out by force, because I realized, and I think they did
also, that if I was to come out of this illness whole of body
and sound of mind I needed Sister Linden.

A dark sleek paper man swept into the ward every morning

and evening. He brought news of the outside world, not only in the printed pages in his bag, but in his own patter, and I looked forward to his: "Good morning, ladies! How many for the Barmaids' Bible?" with which greeting he invariably made his entrance. It was some time before I realized that the "Barmaids' Bible" was a daily newspaper. A man with a built-up boot came to do the polishing, making a treacherous mirror of the floor, which was a death-trap to the patients, a source of constant annoyance to skidding nurses, and an indignity to the doctors who, more than once, measured their length on it. I even saw the head physician make a three-point landing under a patient's bed.

Twice a week a double-decker bookcase, laden with library books, was wheeled in to the ward by a voluntary hospital worker, whose personality left a lasting impression on all patients, even if the matter they chose to read did not. Porters and orderlies trekked in and out with kitchen supplies, medical supplies, laundry, mail, cylinders of oxygen, trollies to take patients to the X-ray department or theatre. There were pathologists and radiologists coming and going with X-ray plates, specimens, and laboratory results; physiotherapists, inspection visits from matron or sub-matron, dietitians, and almoners. Then there were the patients' visitors on Wednesday and Sunday. The big doors at the bottom of the ward were always swinging, and I never learnt by what method Sister managed to keep her head above the traffic and steer a straight course to the most urgent of a dozen different problems, all demanding attention.

There was a sharp dividing line between the world of my illness and the world before my illness—that was inevitable; but it did not mean that I had stepped across a line dividing light from darkness, or joy from sorrow. "Ifs" and "buts" were of little interest, unless they referred to the future, and I was kept too busy to have time to indulge in reminiscences.

It was in the last days of September that Sister told me I had to be moved.

"You will be going to the Casualty ward, for three weeks. We are closing this ward for spring-cleaning."

"You will come and see me, Sister?"

"My dear, I cannot trespass on another Sister's ward. Anyway, I shan't have time. I'll be busy here cleaning up."

So with Jimmy in his frame, and me in Jimmy, we left Sister Linden for the ground floor, where we were taken through some doors into a small Casualty ward adjoining the main orthopaedic one. My bed had gone before us, and it stood rearing its monstrous head in the corner: but to my surprise it did not look out of place, as it did in Alex. Then I realized why. The orthopaedic patients apparently outnumbered the beds in the main ward, and had overflowed into Casualty, for there were two other four-poster arrangements in the room besides my own.

I did not settle in too well that first evening. I could not, because it was a Friday and, at ten o'clock, things began to hum around the unoccupied bed next to me. A patient who had taken an overdose of drugs was carried in, and put to bed. But they had used a stomach pump on her to remove the poison, and, with a large proportion of the drugs taken out of her system, sleep also had gone. She remained very wide awake all night. She screamed. She fought. She swore. She refused to eat, sleep, or be reasonably merry.

Perez stopped by next morning. "How is it going?"

"Come here, Perez." He came and stood by my bed.

"Closer——" Then, as I saw the look on his face, "But not too close."

"Well?"

I whispered. "Perez, I have quite decided that I'd rather be a polio than a prostitute."

"I didn't know you'd ever considered the alternative."

"Sorry . . . but there's one in the next bed.—Tried to poison herself, and she's only young. It's tragic, isn't it?"

"Yes, it is. And, as you seem to have realized, she's in the clutches of something far worse than you." Then he grinned. "But I don't expect you'd get her to believe that."

Chapter 13

A GRANDMOTHER WITH GUTS

━━━━━━━━━━⚬⚬⚬⚬⚬⚬❨⦿❩⚬⚬⚬⚬⚬⚬⚬━━━━━━━━━

I saw things in that Casualty ward that made my heart ache. On my left was a girl who had jumped out of a second-storey window, injuring both her unborn baby and her leg: and the horror of it was that relief at the loss of her baby far outweighed any grief for the amputation of her foot. Opposite her was a dainty sweet-faced patient who was, by nature, a gentle little person but who, because schizophrenia had split her personality, was sometimes an uncontrollable, intractable, and frightening apparition. She was always making crosses to save my soul: crosses cut in the bottom of egg-shells, placed on her locker so that the light from the window shone through them; crosses arranged in cherry stones on her dessert plate; crosses carved in her cake of soap; and she would fix me with an oddly intense gaze, for minutes at a time, with her arms held up in the sign of a cross. She was taken away by two people to an observation hospital, pending certification: the prostitute was taken away by two policemen in plain clothes. I thanked God that it was my body only that was stricken.

Opposite me was one patient I could look at with undisturbed amusement. Everyone called her "Gran". I never knew her other name. She was ninety-four, and had fallen and broken her leg while at an Ideal Home Exhibition. She was the embodiment of Shakespeare's seventh age of man—"sans teeth, sans eyes, sans taste, sans everything". But she had grit: we all marvelled at her grit, and the very essence of it made her one of the most cantankerous, but lovable, old ladies I had ever met. Gran was deaf, she was almost blind, she was very

154

tiny, but she gave no evidence of that pathetic leanness which so often accompanies old age. It was not for some time that I discovered she was as bald as she was deaf.

Before lights were switched on in the morning, and after they were extinguished at night, there were mysterious, but quite audible, rustlings from Gran's bed, as if she were crushing crisp paper between her hands. Then, one morning, the lights came on before she was prepared and I caught her red-handed at her rustling. She had two finely fluffy wisps of white hair on either temple. She carefully unfurled these remnants of past glory, and disclosed, to my astounded gaze, two neat lengths of butter-paper in which she had rolled what remained of her hair. The switch was three inches wide and about a foot long; the hair was fine, but plentiful. She combed and brushed its straightness; then, with the speed and accuracy of a coiffeur, twisted it over and round her bald pate.

She had beady eyes, a sharp chin, a thin nose, and a mouth that betokened a merry life. Her head sat well on her old shoulders as she looked about her like a keen little ferret, but a very dear one—because she was not at all ferrety by nature.

The hotch-potch that comprised her bed was beyond imagining. She was propped up by a back rest, against which lay an assorted and multitudinous collection of bundles which Gran called cushions. More of these were tucked around her hips, she had another pillow under the knee of her good leg which, in its turn, must have a cradle over it to withstand the weight of bedclothes, and she had a "special" pillow on which to rest her beswitched head. This still left her damaged leg. ... There were two pillows bunched under her thigh to counteract draughts, a piece of pinkish flannel was pulled over her plastered suspended foot, and over all a light woollen shawl was draped with care.

The making of Gran's bed was a nightmare for the nurses, particularly as Gran had her own ideas as to what constituted comfort. Her bed was always left until it could be avoided no longer. Often, after a half-hour's struggle, she would still be protesting that she was not quite comfortable. There was only one nurse who had taken and found her measure. She was a minx: blonde and brown-eyed, but she must be given credit for managing the old tartar. She would walk briskly to the bed, place her mouth against Gran's ear, then, with grim determination in her tone and a twinkle in her eye, would bellow:

"Now, Gran, the expert is here. You know me. I'm the expert, and any expert can fix your bed in a jiffy."

There would follow a rapid, but capable, pummelling of pillows and rearranging of bedclothes, and an insistent voice demanding: "You're comfortable now, aren't you? Nobody but an expert should be at this job, but I'm an expert, and you're comfortable, aren't you?"

"Yes, dear, quite comfortable, thank you." Gran's reply astounded us all, it was so submissively polite.

One morning she had been running the gauntlet for almost two hours when Dr Abbott appeared, to conduct his morning round. He caught her imperious tones, strode towards the bed, and yelled:

"Now, Gran, what's all this fuss? What is the matter with you?"

"Oh, doctor, I'm not comfortable." The angry tones subsided somewhat, but she still sounded aggrieved. "My back's not comfortable."

The doctor pulled her forwards onto his chest, took the nearest pillow to hand, puffed it up a little, replaced it, and gently eased her back onto it. "How's that?"

A benign smile spread over Gran's countenance. "Oh, doctor, that's lovely." Her answer was coy.

Dr Abbott waggled his notebook at her and smiled. "Gran," he shouted, "you are a naughty old devil."

She chuckled delightedly.

After that the nurses ruthlessly made and remade her bed, impervious to her grumblings, and when her complaints became unendurable Dr Abbott would be summoned to tuck a corner of her bedclothes in, or smooth out a crease. Sometimes he had only to smile at her to pacify her.

Then one morning an unusual white-coated figure approached Gran's bed. It was unusual in that it enveloped a female form. "Are you the patient requiring chiropody treatment?"

Gran stiffened to attention. "Beg pardon?"

"Are you the patient requiring chiropody treatment?"

"What? Speak up—I'm deaf."

The woman in the long white coat leant closer, and yelled: "Are you the patient requiring chiropody treatment?"

"Ah—chiropody you say. What in the name of all these fandangled new things might that be?"

There was a further process of yelled answer and puzzled questioning, until Gran finally decided that she was not the patient requiring chiropody treatment. But, two days later, she announced to Dr Abbott that her corns were troubling her, and demanded that she receive attention from the chiropodist. No matter how often she was told that she had no corns requiring treatment, no matter how busy they told her the chiropodist was, Gran must have her.

The chiropodist arrived with a trayful of sharp, glinting scalpels, and an expression of tolerance for her humbugging patient. She pushed back the covers from the good leg to disclose a horny old foot such as one could not aspire to possess under the age of ninety. She scraped, and chipped, collecting such a pile of dead yellowish débris that it was to be marvelled there was any foot left. Gran chirruped like a cricket, waggled her foot about, and declared that it was as new as any babe's.

Gran was given food of a more delicate variety than was customary. She would have none of it. A small plateful of steamed fish that was her supper would vanish like lightning.

"Nurse, bring me something solid to eat. I can't exist on baby food."

It would be brought and, in addition to her special light diet, she consumed steamed suet puddings, unpalatable sausages, dumplings, pastries, and all manner of indigestible messes. She survived to good intent. She did something no one ever suspected her of doing again. At ninety-four, and after a severe fracture of the leg, she walked out of hospital assisted only by a stick—a grand old lady.

The evening of the day Gran walked out a visitor was shown

to my bedside; a small, but neatly made man with a dark, clever face, his white coat replaced by the uniform of the Royal Air Force. I could scarcely believe my eyes.

"Doctor Stroobant!"

A shy smile, and a gentle voice. "Well, June?"

"Very well, thank you. You're very lucky I can't use my arms."

"Why?"

"I'd probably throw them round you. Tell me—where have you been? What have you been doing? Why are you here? And why the get-up?"

"Steady on—one thing at a time."

We brought each other up to date, then I let him examine me, as he would, and did my utmost to make an immovable body move in an endeavour to prove to him that he had not stood, in the eleventh hour, by the side of something that was not worth saving. He praised, enthusiastically, my left hand, all the fingers of which were now moving weakly.

"What about your back?"

"I don't know. Mr Muir is coming tomorrow to test it. You came a day too soon."

"I'll come in and see what the result is. I'm on leave for a few days. Good luck for tomorrow."

"I shall need it. Good night."

My two physios left me to rest the following morning, not arriving until after lunch, accompanied by the head of their department, Mr Muir, and Dr Abbott. I was quickly transferred into Jimmy's better half and Mr Muir began his examination. It took a long time, and I had no idea whether there were things favourable, or unfavourable, to be found in my back because I could not see the big man's expression. I doubt if I should have been any the wiser if I could have seen it.

He dug his hands systematically up and down my spine, while I attempted to carry out his directions, then the physios set up the battery and he prodded about with an electrode. Dr Abbott bent over a chart, putting down numbers as Mr Muir called them. I did not like the electrical test. The current bored through the flesh into my bones like a dentist's drill in the

decayed part of a tooth, but it eventually came to an end. I was relieved to be back in Jimmy, and to find the big man still beside my bed.

I looked up at him. "Well?"

He shook his head. "Nothing."

"Thank you."

"You like things straight from the shoulder, don't you?"

"Yes, I do."

"Hm—now let me see those fingers."

I fluttered my five digits at him. I could manage an apologetic clawing and unclawing movement; I could separate them a little; and bring them together again.

"What about opponens?"

I brought my little finger across my hand, towards my thumb. They did not meet, but there was something there.

He allowed a smile to flicker for an instant. "So—you are learning the correct names for things. I wondered."

"I'm struggling in a morass of Latin, but the physios are a great help."

"It's good practice for them, too. June, I am very pleased with that hand. It has possibilities."

"Oh, Mr Muir, I wish it was my foot."

The slopes of his eyebrows knit in a heavy frown and his voice was stern. "When you are a little older, and a little wiser, my dear girl, you will realize that it is far better to have the use of your hands than your feet."

"Why?"

"Because the co-ordination of mind, eye, and hand, is of the greatest importance if one wishes to do something useful. Feet don't enter into it." He looked down at his own, and back to me, the sternness gone from his face. "But I must admit, they come in handy."

Perez came at six carrying a small glass dish that contained some fruit set in jelly.

"With Sister Linden's compliments. Shall I give it to you now?"

"Yes, please, Perez."

"What did Mr Muir have to say?"

"Sorry, old chap, he said there was nothing there."

He spoon-fed me in silence, and I ate in silence, for some time.

"Do you want to talk about it, June—or shall we leave it?"

"I don't know. . . . Could you tell me something, though? What will the outcome be if my back does not recover?"

Perez was a very sick man. He was also a doctor or, at least, so near to being one that it made little difference. He had a brilliant brain, and he loved life with such absorption that no matter seemed too great or small for the range of his sympathy. I could talk to him about anything because he could approach it from the point of view of patient, doctor, counsellor and friend. He never shelved any question that he was capable of answering—and there were very few of mine that he could not answer. His greatest virtue, in my eyes, was that he did not drip pity out of every pore.

He looked at me now.

"Well, if your back doesn't recover, it simply means a spinal carriage for the rest of your life."

"A spinal carriage! One of those things like a big clothes basket on wheels?"

"Yes. But you can get about in them, you know. There's a handle behind the patient's head, for pushing."

"You mean I'll have to be pushed about?" And as he nodded. "Just between you and me, Perez, I am not going to be pushed about in a spinal carriage for the rest of my life."

"Who says so?"

"I say so. And there's an end to it. I've made up my mind. Back, or no back . . ."

"Most illogical, but it has my wholehearted concurrence. You stick to your ideas. Look, I think, if you don't mind, I'll go up to Alex and tell Sister. She'll still be there."

Two days later Alexandra ward was reopened. My physios were late in arriving, and they eased the heavy weight of the electrical equipment onto my locker with a sigh.

"Well . . . we thought you'd be up in Alex, and we've hawked this thing all the way up there, just to be told you were still here. What goes on?"

"I don't know. I expected to be back myself, but perhaps they're waiting until they've settled down a bit."

I was still in the Casualty ward when the physios returned after lunch and, as I had not been moved by evening, I began to think that someone, somehow, did not intend that I should.

I slept the night in Casualty; I spent the next day in Casualty; and, as night staff replaced the day, I began for the first time to wish that I could walk two flights of stairs with Jimmy in my arms, set him down on the floor of Alex, climb into him, and sleep.

The morning of the third day the Medical Superintendent walked in. He was, I suppose, the answer to any nurse's prayer, for he was tall, blue-eyed, with black curly hair, and a persuasive lop-sided smile. He was in his early thirties, and he was a bachelor. He looked very surprised to see me.

"Please, Doctor Anstiss, help me." I would not have minded if he had been covered with warts, or hair had been growing out of his ears; he was the Medical Superintendent, and he obviously expected me to be back in Alexandra ward.

He came and stood at the foot of my bed, rocking gently back and forth on his feet. "What is the matter, June? You look as if the bottom had fallen out of the world. I have never seen you so dismal." He had an easy, unharassed way of speaking.

"I want to go back to Alex. I don't want to make a fuss, but if you think a few tears and some noise will get me anywhere, I could easily produce them."

"I have no doubt you could—but I don't think it will be necessary." He went out quietly: everything about him was quiet, but it was a restrained quietness that was proof of his tenacity and sincerity. I waited happily, albeit a little doubtfully.

After some time my physios arrived. "We met Doctor Anstiss in the hall, and he said to tell you that there is a corner of Alex marked off with a large red cross, all ready to receive you."

I was trundled back to Alex on a trolley, with my four-poster hard on our heels. The ward was fresh and bright: and it was home. A junior was scraping fluff off the bottoms of the chair legs with her scissors; Staff Nurse was standing at an instrument tray, filling a hypodermic syringe; Dr Longsdale and Sister had their heads bent over some medical reports. Sister looked up quickly and came racing towards us.

"Mind the paint!" Her hands were raised in horror, as was her voice. "Don't you dare take any of my new paint off."

I found myself in one of the three top bed spaces of the ward, where I had a window all to myself, and, through it, a large reach of sky. I also had a view of the entire ward. Everything looked so spick and span that I realized I must be a sizeable blot on the landscape, but I did not care particularly. I also realized that I had been very selfish, but I did not care about that either, at least, not sufficiently to sacrifice my personal wishes.

Chapter 14

A QUIZ SESSION

~~~~~~~~~~~~~~~~~~●~~~~~~~~~~~~~~~~~~

The only recognizable face among the patients was that of the Hungarian, Mrs Manning. She was shuffling about in a powder blue dressing-gown, and when she saw that I was alone, she crossed slowly to my bed. She was even more beautiful at close quarters.

"Hallo," she said. "I come to visit Jeemmy and June, if you please. He is a funny fellow, yes? He cannot speak, of English, one word. Can he speak, I wonder, in my language?" She babbled a vast amount of foreign words in a wheedling tone, then she gave up. "Jeemmy, I think, is no good. He is what you English call a—a dumb—dumb—dumb-bell." She threw up her hands and laughed. "That is what he is—a dumb-bell. Jeemmy dumb-bell."

She was still laughing when Staff Nurse came up the ward, to place a bunch of flowers on my chest. They were wrapped in florists' paper pinned together at the bottom. She placed my hand close to the pin.

"Can you manage, June?"

"Yes, nurse, thank you."

I laughed delightedly, for it was the first time I had been left by myself to pull a pin out of a piece of paper. I grabbed it by the head and gave it a tentative jerk, but as nothing happened, apart from a loud crackle where my hand lay on the paper, I tried a really gargantuan wrench. The pin still stuck.

There was silence in the ward, except for the rustle of that cursed paper. I looked up. All eyes were on the bunch of flowers on my raised bed, and Mrs Manning was now standing by my side wringing her hands, her eyes imploring me to let her help me. It was the pity in all those eyes that I did not like.

163

I tried to twist the pin round to loosen it, but it would not even oblige me by twisting.

"Please——" came a small voice at my side.

"No, thank you." My hand was shaking badly, I was sweating, and I was furious. If something doesn't happen soon, I thought, I'll start howling in sheer bad temper. I tried corkscrew tactics. I tried to take it slowly: I tried to take it by surprise. But still it stuck.

"Excuse me, Mrs Manning. I've got to give this girl an injection." Staff Nurse's brisk voice startled both of us.

"Sorry, nurse, I move."

Screens were pushed round me. I goggled in surprise. "What do I have to have an injection for, nurse?"

"You don't have to have one, you twerp," she whispered.

"Then why——"

"My dear girl, if you'd gone on playing with that pin much longer we'd have had a lunatic, as well as a polio, on our hands."

I laughed my relief. "You're quite right. I was ready to go stark, staring mad."

There was no sound of rustling paper as she pulled that silly silver thing out. "And now. I'll lay it on the top—so, and then, when the screens are down you can make it look as if you are taking it out. But you'll have to act as if it is a struggle."

She walked away with the syringe, then returned to remove the screens. The battle was on again. I do not know whether those patients guessed what had happened and would not have me know, or whether Nurse's strategy, and my acting, deceived them, but there was a relieved sigh, and a round of smiles, as I called out that I had got it out. I spent the next half-hour pushing it in and pulling it out of my bedclothes, which was most enjoyable, until Sister reminded me that hospital linen was made for the purpose of covering patients, not for them to poke holes in.

As well as a new coat of paint Alexandra sported a new batch of nurses; a new group of medical students; and the new houseman, Dr Longsdale, a tall, sandy-haired young man who walked with a peculiar sliding gait, his shoulders slightly hunched and his head making a forward stabbing movement at every step, rather like a boxer in the ring.

On the evening of my return I lay reading, with a book propped up on my stand, when Dr Longsdale appeared at my bedside. "What's the knitting needle for?" he asked.

"To turn the pages of my book."

My hand was lying directly beneath the book so I caught the needle, as firmly as I could, between my first two fingers, inserted the point between two pages, and flipped one over.

"How long have you been doing that?"

I laughed. "Just the last two days, and I'm afraid I'm so proud of myself that I sometimes don't read the entire page. I've been guilty of skipping whole pages in this particular book. I get a turning-over craze every now and then, and don't stop to give myself a chance to read."

"June, do you—oh, no, it doesn't matter. I really came to ask if I may look at Jimmy's better half, as I understand this anterior shell of yours is called."

He was underneath the planks of my bed for some time, and after a series of bumps, bangs, coughing, and laboured breathing he crawled out, stood erect, dusted his hands, then made some polite conversation before leaving me.

The following morning when I told my physios about his curiosity they bent down to ascertain that all was well with the headless one. There was a startled exclamation, a burst of laughter, the cast was pulled out, and stood up: then it was turned to face me. Jimmy's better half was resplendent in a two-piece bathing costume of tropical design and colour. It had been drawn with indelible grease crayons, and there was nothing we could do to erase it. The woman had been clothed, and there was no possible way of disentangling her draperies. I could not decide whether it made her more respectable or not.

I was glad that the physios had replaced her under the bed because Mr Muir broke in upon us in the middle of treatment. My legs were aloft: the physios were bent over my left hand.

"Well?" Hands tucked neatly in his pockets he towered above us. The physios straightened up quickly.

"Mr Muir—what do you think? I can bend my elbow, only a fraction, but I can bend it."

His eyebrows lifted. "What did you say you could do, young lady?"

"Bend my elbow."

He crossed to the other side of the bed and examined my arm. I could bend it about an inch.

"That's splendid. You will be able to feed yourself when that is a little stronger, because your forearm will be free to swing between your plate and your mouth. You will have to practise handling a fork, or a spoon."

"Could I use my fingers if I can't hold a fork or spoon?"

"Yes." He broke into a short rumble of laughter. "But didn't Sister tell me that you are very fond of jelly?"

At lunch time I endeavoured to propel my food into my mouth by means of my first two fingers. Nurse cut my meat and vegetables for me, and sometimes helped me move my hand towards my face. It was slow, but it was a beginning. All my food henceforth came to me cut in cubes, or in some manageable form. Usually my hand gave in before my stomach was full, but the nurses did what I could not and they never hurried me, although, often, it must have tried their patience to see me slowly manœuvring elusive scraps of food in a shaky path across the bedclothes, over my chin, and into my gaping mouth.

Jimmy became a garbage tin for every particle of food that failed to reach its goal. It was completely bewildering, the cunning way that pieces could avoid my mouth, tumble over my chin, round my neck, eventually to lodge themselves between my back and Jimmy's interior. A constant itch was sufficient evidence of their resting-place. Staff Nurse failed to understand how it all accumulated until her curiosity drove her to experiment herself. Off duty one night she stretched herself out on the floor of her room, and asked her room-mate to hold a biscuit for her, in such a position that she could eat it without lifting, turning, or moving, her head in any way. She admitted that there was a considerable pile of crumbs to sweep up, even after one biscuit.

I fed Jimmy well, but not wisely. Very late one night I called softly to Nurse, who tip-toed to my bedside.

"May I have a drink, please, nurse. I'm terribly thirsty," I whispered.

"Yes, of course. If you wait a moment I'll bring you a cup of tea, if you don't mind having it out of a feeding cup—then I won't have to put the light on."

Nurse quickly reappeared, holding a white china object with a thick straight spout. She stood by my side talking in whispers, the cup in her hands. I did not like to remind her to give me a drink so let her talk, until she said:

"Have you had enough?"

I was amazed. "Nurse, I haven't had any."

"What? Are you sure you haven't had any?"

"Yes, nurse, quite sure."

"Well, where on earth has it gone to? I've been pouring it somewhere."

We were both trying to suppress our mirth but snorts and stifled gusts of laughter echoed through the ward. She switched on her torch to locate the source of disappearance. She had been holding the spout of the cup between my shoulder and Jimmy, thinking they were my top lip and bottom teeth. The entire contents had formed a puddle under my right shoulder-blade, and, as the tea was lukewarm, there had been no sudden change in temperature to warn me of what was happening. Night Staff was called. She threw up her hands in despair.

"Jimmy will have to go to the drying-room, immediately, before the plaster cracks or air bubbles develop—what a job at this hour of the night!"

Nurse and I need not have bothered to whisper to each other. Lights were switched into sudden brightness; the telephone jangled; a mattress was dragged from somewhere; sheet, draw-sheet, and pillows were stacked on it; porters tramped in noisily; voices instructing; feet scuffling; arms heaving; and I was removed from Jimmy. He and his frame were scraped across planks and dropped none too gently onto the floor, the mattress was jockeyed into position, the body lowered, and

167

nurses made up the bed, while porters beat a heavy exit with Jimmy.

"I don't think we ought to make any further attempts to give Jimmy a drink, nurse, do you?" I asked.

Early next morning a sliding step coming up the ward warned me of Dr Longsdale's approach. "Well, how do you feel, now that you are out of Jimmy's clutches?"

"Not very happy."

He looked surprised. "Why, June? Sore?"

"Yes, very—and backachy. But it doesn't matter. It's not for long."

He stroked the back of his head. "Well, I wanted you to drink a lot today, and that will mean of course——"

"Extra beeps. But why do I have to drink a lot? I drink gallons as it is."

"Yes, I know, but they want some extra specimens for the path lab."

I was flabbergasted. "But I've got rid of all my bugs. There is nothing wrong with my specimens."

"That's why they want them. The lab, as you may imagine, is never at a loss for specimens that give evidence of disease in reaction to chemical tests." He waved his hand at the other patients in the ward. "But in order to understand the significance of such tests the students must have a normal specimen for comparison. So, you see——"

"What's it to be—water?"

"With lemon—unsweetened—if you can take it."

It was certainly not a very difficult, nor a very delicate, task, but it was comforting to feel that in some small measure I was considered useful.

In the late afternoon Sister came to ask me if I was sufficiently dehydrated to go out onto the balcony for an hour or two.

"Yes, Sister, I'd love to go."

"It will probably be your last chance, as the days are getting colder and we shall soon be into fogs."

"I'm longing to see a pea-souper. I've heard so much about them."

"The first one will be enough for you, I should think."

It was strange to be bounced along without Jimmy: I was missing him. My plane tree was no longer green. Tattered leaves of yellow and rust sober-toned against a murky sky; no wheeling gulls; jabs of black chimney-pots making an irregular silhouette. But all that mattered was that I had been left on my own. I could not go out and find solitude: I had to be taken to it and left. It did not happen often or for long, because it could not, but what I had was made doubly precious by its rareness.

As I was spoilt by the people within St Mary's, so I was by those who came from without: my visitors. To dance constant attendance upon a sick bed, whose occupant was previously unknown, is, I should imagine, dull and difficult, and when that sick bed retains its occupant month after month, especially so. I never lacked visitors. In fact, at the beginning, before I had sorted everyone out, I often found myself surrounded by a group of people who neither knew me, nor one another. But they were all splendid: Stephen's aristocratic-looking uncle and his gentle aunt; a family I met through Rotary; lots of young people from the Royal College of Music, among them, of course, was Gray; representatives of various organizations; friends and relations of my friends and relations; and an extremely attractive friend of someone I knew in the Akaroa Peninsula—she always knew the right things to say, and do, but it was months before she told me that she had a son who was an Oxford Blue, and who had lost both his legs in the war.

I was often at a loss to know how the dozens of people who found their way to my bedside ever came to hear about me. They were from all walks of life, and, added to the diversity in the patients around me, and the hospital staff, I claimed to have met the greatest cross-section of English people that it was possible to meet. After being discharged from hospital patients themselves came to visit me, and what astonished and gratified me was the fact that all these people did not come just once, say their piece, and trot off—they kept coming. It humbled me, although I do not know why.

From the affection and esteem which I developed for my English visitors grew my love for England. A country is its people, and I came to know England very well. But in the learning process it was inevitable that I should rub shoulders with those on the other side, who were both scared and horrified by the picture I presented. There were a few—very few—who thought my life was ruined, and fewer still who gave voice to their thoughts.

After about twenty minutes of rapid questioning on the part of one of my visitors, begrudging answers on mine, and depression settling in more heavily as she learnt the extent of my paralysis, I was willing to do almost anything to stop her verbal exploration of my body. Even if she had come to visit me, it was my body, and I did not see what business it was of hers to probe its possibilities. I had just made up my mind to ask her how much housekeeping money her husband allowed her per week, when she stood up and leant over me, close to my face.

"June," she said, very earnestly, "you are a sensible girl . . . don't you really think, all things considered, that you would be better dead?"

That floored me completely. I had never considered whether it would be better if I were dead: I just did not want to die. Then I started to laugh, and the more I thought about it, the more I laughed. My visitor waited in some bewilderment.

"Sorry," I said, when I had myself in hand again, "but you must see the irony of it. When I could have died quite easily, the people in this hospital kept me alive, and now I can't die unless I commit suicide, and how am I going to do that? Fancy being so badly paralysed that you can't commit suicide if you feel like it——" But she did not smile.

Then there was the bright spark who knew that I had polio, who had visited me on several occasions, and who, when faced with a picture of planks, frame, Jimmy, me, Balkan beam, slings, springs, ropes, and pulleys, placed a hot clammy hand on my inert one, and said: "My dear, can you walk?"

"Yes," I said. "I trot round the ward twice before breakfast every day."

"Well, that's marvellous. I'm so glad."

That, I thought, is meant for a joke, so I merely laughed. It was certainly not my intention to mislead my visitor, because I thought anybody would know that if a polio could walk they would not be lying encased in plaster in a hospital. To my consternation the news was spread, and I was forced to throw a damper on my congratulators, and apologetically retract my statement.

Many people asked me what it felt like to be in an iron lung. That was understandable, and I answered them as truthfully as I could, but I did not see why I should be asked, as if I was a museum exhibit that had found a voice, what it felt like to be paralysed. I could only say that it gave me a paralysed feeling—which was the truth. If anyone had a leg off, I suppose they would feel as if they only had one leg. I could not understand why they had to introduce the subject of paralysis, anyway, when there were so many other things to talk about.

At the end of a particularly tiring day of treatment a visitor was ushered to my bedside just as I was about to close my eyes and rest my weary brain. I had not even had my tea, but I pulled myself together, and made, as I conceitedly imagined, an effort to be bright. After ten minutes of question and answer, thought dragged heavily, and my laughter was forced.

"I'm so sorry," I said, "but I'm a bit tired and can't think straight. You will have to excuse me."

"Are you, my dear?"

"Yes." I felt rather poorly about dismissing her thus, but I was grateful that she had understood, and was leaving me alone. I closed my eyes: then I felt, rather than heard, that she had come closer to me. I anticipated a consoling kiss.

"My dear, you don't have to explain to me. I understand fully, and I know you must get these little fits of depression, and long for all the things that you have lost."

I opened my eyes smartly. "Whatever are you talking about?"

"You must often long to get up and walk about again, and dance, and play games, as you used to, and the thought must depress you. You are just a little depressed now, aren't you? You needn't pretend with me."

"Have you ever been paralysed?"

She looked startled. "No."

"Well, how do you know what you're talking about?"

In a detached corner of my mind I realized that I had managed not to swear.

All I received was an unctuous smile. "I'll sit by you for a little while, until it passes."

"It", I supposed, was my fit of depression, which I had yet to experience. She stayed an hour, and when she had gone I felt I must tell Sister, because the inevitable reaction to large doses of pity is self-pity, and I did not want to start feeling sorry for myself. My understanding friend must be struck off the visiting list. Fortunately Sister did not know how to swear, because she did not hold anything back. She was magnificent. . . .

I suppose it was because my days were fully occupied with treatment and any spare night hours with the thought-wave practice to my paralysed muscles, that I was unable to look at myself objectively. Sometimes I was startled into a temporary awareness of my situation by a look, sometimes a gesture, sometimes a word. I was grateful because it goaded me on, although I wished with all my heart that people would not worry themselves wondering what life had in store for me. Dead or alive, no one knows the answer to that.

In endeavouring to sort things out for me, and plan my future, one lady in a confiding, and somewhat embarrassed, tone indicated that she wanted to ask me something that had been worrying her. "You don't have to answer it."

"Fire ahead," I said.

"Well, I just wondered, June—could you have babies?"

I was speechless. You, I thought, undoubtedly take the prize.

"Babies?" I repeated in an asinine way, but the mere fact of having said something brought everything into focus again, and I found half a dozen questions I could put to her rushing to my shameless tongue. I was glad I looked at her before I spoke again because what I saw in her face pulled me up short. You poor little thing, I thought, life for you means a husband, children, and a home. Apart from that nothing. And accordingly, if I am to live, I must be able to have babies. She was waiting, not impatiently, but in some trepidation, for my reply.

"Yes," I said, "I could have babies." I was not at all sure on this point myself, but at that moment it did not matter to me whether I could, or could not, and I did not want her to go away feeling unhappy.

"I'm so glad." Her relief was evident in the smile she gave me, but I had no mind to pursue the topic so we talked of other things. That was not her last visit, because I felt she had not come to pity.

Although I loathed pity because of the circumstances that produced it, I could not justifiably bear umbrage against the very small percentage of my visitors who gave expression to it, for the simple reason that I did not know what my reactions would have been, had our positions been reversed. Cripples had always embarrassed me because they made me ashamed of my own healthy, vigorous limbs; but now that I was seeing the situation through the other end of the telescope I realized what an ass I had been. Even if I was unable to move, I enjoyed watching movement in others, and I was sorry when people were embarrassed to such a degree by my immobility that they could not look me straight in the eye. There were thousands who had a greater burden to bear than I had, but because it was not possible to split them open with a scalpel, to reveal their disease-ridden interiors, they were not pitied. I came to the conclusion that poliomyelitis was a nice clean disease to have. Of all the diseases I saw in St Mary's it was by far the healthiest. I tried to explain this to my visitors for, in truth, I loved them all. They were a necessity because they prevented me from becoming hospitalized: their attitude towards me was different; the impact of ordinary civilian dress in a world of uniforms was always startling; and the constant reminder of life outside the walls of Alexandra ward prevented me from becoming utterly absorbed in what went on within immediate reach of my senses.

Chapter 15

I ACQUIRE 3-D VISION

~~~~~vvvnnⱱ🇴ꞁⱱnnvv~~~~~

With November came the grey skies, and the fogs, carrying in creeping, drifting smoke. Sister was quite right, for, after the first excitement of watching the soupy whirling mistiness, I became conscious only of the clogging aftermath: black grit in my nose; sore throats; and smuts everywhere. I realized why the nurses wore black shoes and stockings, and coloured uniforms, and why we had dark green bed-spreads over us. It worked its way about like a nasty pernicious disease, seeping through cracks and ventilators, leaving an unwholesome reminder wherever it went.

It left me with a cold that brought considerable distress to my breathing mechanism. I was kept awake all one night so that I could concentrate on inhaling and exhaling—it was either that, or the lung. This incident upset me, because I was blissfully unaware that my breathing was still very weak, but I was thankful for it, because it served to impress upon me the exceedingly slow and unspectacular recovery of paralysed muscles; something that I was only just beginning to admit myself, although I had been told about it often enough. Dr Timms had told me, Mr Muir had told me, Perez had told me, but my ideas of a long time in hospital extended no further than six months. Now, in my eighth month, I made up my mind to stop asking them when they thought I should be well again.

Despite fogs, and my forceful awakening to the slowness of my recovery, November was a happy month because, one night, I was taken on a trolley to a concert given by the pianist Eileen Joyce in the medical school. Matron produced a very pretty, fuzzy green bed-jacket from somewhere and, although

I had to wear it back to front because Jimmy would not allow anything to come between him and me, I felt as excited as I had when I put on my first evening frock. Mrs Venning, with the spontaneous generosity that characterizes so many Cockneys, brought a beautiful spray of pink carnations and fern to pin on the jacket, and stayed in the ward, when she should have been off duty, to see me being taken away. She looked so proudly at the entourage, as it went through the door with Perez at its head, that any onlooker could quite easily have believed that she had been personally responsible for all of us, and the concert as well. Eileen Joyce will never know the joy she gave to one member of her audience that night, because it was the first music I had heard since my admission to hospital, and I loved music.

Going down in the lift to the underground tunnel that connected the medical school with the main hospital, Perez pulled at one of my plaits. I looked up at him.

"Didn't know you were so fond of music, June. Why didn't you tell us before?"

"I didn't know you had concerts like this."

"Well, now you've made your début, I'll see that you go when there's anything decent on."

I do not know whether it was the sight of Eileen Joyce's fingers bouncing about on those piano keys, or, as is more probable, the unremitting efforts of the physios, that gave strength to my fingers, but next day I made some headway with a fork. I had been trying to put an end to fingering my food but the strength required to hold a fork, jab it into food, then convey the load to my mouth, had been beyond me. The position of my plate became problematical because I did not want the nurses to have to stand over me and hold it. The only safe place was on my chest, which made the task of dropping food into my mouth reasonably easy, because my head was held downwards, and backwards, by Jimmy, and I had gravity to assist me. If my hand did quiver and fail in mid-air it ought to fall onto my face, or near enough to it, to enable me to push the fork up and over my chin. What was impossible was for me to see what was on my plate because my eyes were below its level. It was like a "lucky dip": I decided that we must all be too well fed in New Zealand, because it seemed to me that my luck was invariably out.

I was very proud of myself that day. My food was cut into the customary cubes which I speared with prongs, then carefully propelled towards my mouth that was agape with grinning. When it came to supper-time Nurse balanced my plate on my chest, and giggled.

"What is it, nurse?"

She put the handle of the fork between my first and second fingers. "I'm not telling you. See how you make out." She hurried away still giggling.

Without the slightest knowledge of what was on my plate, I felt cautiously around it, with my fork. I encountered a softish ooze which, upon contact, immediately moved away, to leave me probing my cutlery on china. The more fiercely I sought for something substantial to eat, the more unresisting the food became. Even the plate seemed to have developed a tendency to sliminess. I tenderly explored the most solid portion and, with a twist that one uses in gaffing fish, I succeeded in landing something. My mouth was open in anticipation, and remained so in amazement as a shaky, tenuous wriggle of orangey-white followed my fork through the air. We were having spaghetti in tomato sauce for supper.

I paused midway, at a loss how to proceed. My hand was trembling badly; the fork was halfway between the plate and my mouth; and the spaghetti streamed behind, with one end still on the plate, and the other on the fold-back of the sheet. I tried to raise my arm high enough to release the straggling piece, then made a haphazard plunge towards my mouth. The fork jabbed my palate, and the spaghetti lay in a limp orange-coloured stream over my chin and the bedclothes. But I had my teeth into some of it. I sucked in noisily, filled my mouth, and left a bright weal of tomato sauce over everything.

Nurse was still laughing as she washed my face.

"What's so funny?" I asked.

"You never saw anything to equal you and Mrs Jones in the small ward, eating your respective suppers tonight."

"What's the matter with Mrs Jones? Can't she feed herself properly?"

Nurse was changing my sheet. "She is suffering from a type of motor aphasia. She knows what she wants to do, and say, but she can't produce the words, or actions, that she wants. She knew perfectly well where her plate was, and where her mouth was, her arm is quite strong, and capable of transferring food from one to the other, but she has lost the power to direct it. There she sat, throwing spaghetti over the locker, the floor—everywhere but in her mouth." She looked up apologetically. "Have I been very unfair to let you both struggle? But it was such a temptation to see who would finish first and who would make the biggest mess."

The following day I was hopefully prodding at my midday meal when a surgeon strode up the ward, to pause at the foot of my bed. He did not attend me but he was a New Zealander, and he popped in from time to time to see if I had everything I wanted. He watched me with a smile. "Can't you see what is on your plate, June?"

"No I can't."

"Hm—perhaps it is as well, but I've got something I think would help." He grimaced at the plate-load as he turned away.

Nurse was collecting the empty crocks when he returned, clasping a small, rectangular, black box in his hand. He opened it, to produce the strangest pair of spectacles I had ever seen.

"These are prismatic glasses. They have three-dimensional lenses, which allow the wearer to perceive what is going on at his feet while he looks straight ahead." He bent over me to fix the shanks behind my ears. On my face they protruded like the headlamps of a motor-car, but I was able, by simply gazing ceiling-wards, to see what was lying on my chest.

Those spectacles brought me great enjoyment, and much amusement. I lay contentedly in Jimmy, the glasses fitted over my eyes, and I saw things I had never been able to see before because of the position of my head. All I could see of Dr Longsdale through the glasses, as he stood close to my head, were his hands fiddling with the disc end of his stethoscope, which was hanging halfway down his body. I did not need to see his face to know that he was astonished.

"What on earth are you doing now, June?"

"Actually, I'm watching your hands mangling that stethoscope." He laughed, and dropped them into the pockets of his white coat. "I can still see them."

"Well, stop looking at them. I've brought a doctor from Scotland to see you."

"Would you remove these spectacles, please? Then I can see him."

He took them off, and I looked up at a square, rugged face topped with unruly bronze hair. Dr Longsdale was holding the glasses in his hand.

"Let's have a look. I say, these would be wonderful things to have in lectures. Just think, I would—to all appearances—be gazing at the Dean, but in reality I could be reading a thriller on my lap." He handed them to the stout man from Scotland.

"Well I'm blessed," he said, as he adjusted them, "I can see my feet!"

Dr Longsdale's mouth tilted at the corners. "First time for years, old chap, I bet." I assumed they were friends of long standing.

Then I discovered that I could write more easily with the aid of the glasses. I had not thought of it at first, but five days after I had been given them I received a letter from my father, with one small sentence in it that told me he was worrying far too much about me. His letters, written in a beautiful script that one unfortunately finds only in the writing of his generation, told me always of the bush, the birds, the river, and the sea. He loved all those things, and wrote intimately and affectionately of them because he had taught me to love them too. His letters came once a week, as did mother's, but they came on different days, mother's at the beginning, and father's at the end of the week so that I should have news from home regularly twice a week. Mother kept me posted with births, deaths, marriages, bazaars, social gossip, and the well-being of the little village where we lived: father left her to it, devoting himself to nature. At this time, when London was dirty, foggy, and

178

damp, his letters were like sunshine, with their descriptions of the native flowers that covered the hillsides with glory as Christmas approached.

At the foot of his letter on this November day, he wrote: "I am wondering, my dear, how you are sleeping in that plaster cast." It was not much, but I knew my father. His was no idle wonder . . . he was worrying himself sick, so I must write and explain more fully about Jimmy, the comfort he gave me, and the aches I developed as soon as I was taken out of him. It was then I discovered that, with the prismatic glasses, I could write a letter with a pad flat on my chest. It was much easier than propping it, and my hand, up at an angle so that I could see.

I wrote a long letter which took me several days, and was very glad because I later had news from mother telling me that my father could not sleep for worrying about whether I was sleeping, but now that he knew all about Jimmy he was much happier. Apart from the fact that I was my mother's daughter, my paralysis threw many burdens upon her shoulders. My father liked to present a stern, unyielding exterior, but he was a sensitive, generous man at heart. I cannot say that my illness distressed him more than my mother, but he was unable to adjust himself to it as well as she could, so she had to push away her own worries in an endeavour to relieve him of his. She also had to pacify friends and relations, and laugh away the doleful predictions as to my subsequent fate. She wrote letters to the English people who wrote to her about me, she kept all my friends in New Zealand informed by post when she could not speak to them, and no matter what her own apprehensions were she had to keep a stiff upper lip and inspire everyone else with hope.

Peter wrote a bulky weekly letter which reached me, usually, on a Friday, and often through the week a card or picture would arrive. Perez had ceased to become a visitor: he was a daily occurrence, and a delight. Once, when I was tired and extraordinarily quiet, I heard Sister asking one of the nurses if Mr Casado had been in to see me and, finding out that he had not, concluded that his absence was the reason for my silence, adding something to the effect that his visits were quite as important a part of my treatment as my exercises.

Although there was little active movement in my body at this time it was moved vigorously every day, because I was having, what my physios called, "full suspension". My entire body was being slung to the beam, and I flailed about in the air, on my ropes and springs, with jerky, unsynchronized movements like a puppet on wires, only sometimes the physios could not control all the strings at once and peculiar things happened. It was all tremendous fun. There was a toggle attached to a spring round each foot; a sling attached to a spring round each knee; a large sling with a spring on either side of it under my seat; a similar one under my back and shoulders; a special one for my head; one round each elbow; and toggles for my hands. The only difficulty that was experienced was in not knowing which end to suspend first. A paralysed body, when it falls, collapses rather like a drunk man. There is no resistance to the fall, and it is therefore carried where gravity takes it, which is downwards—straight and true, in a comfortable relaxed heap.

I was turned into Jimmy's better half twice a week for scrubbing, back massage, and frantic efforts to persuade life into me with electrical stimulus, heat, thought waves, passive movements, pummellings, and anything anyone could think of. Then I was told that I was marvellous. There was nothing marvellous about me: it was my body, and my main interest was in getting it better. But my body did not belong to the physios: yet, they slaved over it, almost willing it to move.

During the first week in December my right fingers began to get a move on, and, one morning as I lay with my right arm well lathered, receiving electrical treatment, Dr Longsdale's face appeared over the screens. He was accustomed to seeing my hand lying idle and useless on the counterpane. It was so wasted that the tendons running from knuckle to wrist stood out, cord-like, from my palm as well as the back of my hand. Activated by the current my fingers were folding and unfolding gently. He watched, fascinated, then invited himself inside the screens to observe the marvel of my moving fingers at closer range. As the muscles were as weak as they could have been, the current required to stimulate activity was a great deal stronger than that required to contract an ordinary muscle. Dr Longsdale turned to one of the physios:

"What would happen," he enquired, "if you applied that current to my arm?"

"Exactly the same as is happening here, only the reaction would be stronger and more spontaneous."

"Mm—I should like to try it."

The physio transferred the discs from my neck and arm to his. He had already rolled up the sleeve of his white coat, exposing a large, hairy forearm, bulging with almost indecent-looking muscle. The physios kept the current turned off until everything was in position. I was about to remind them that they had not reduced the number of milliamps, when I caught the twinkle in the eye of the one who was standing over the apparatus. So, I thought, she intends giving the doctor a current five times the strength that he would normally require. I clenched my teeth, anticipating the shock that he was going to get. His forearm rested on Jimmy's frame, while his other hand lay on the top bar of one of the screens. His face registered the keenest interest. The stage was set and the physios let him have the current. . . .

There was an agonized yell; a belch of heaving muscle doing its utmost to twist into cramp; the screen shot across the floor; and Dr Longsdale, his face transfused with pain, was nursing his arm. He let out an oath, then looked at me:

"I say, June, do you have to put up with that?" His arm dangled limply from the elbow. "Look—I can't use it. I've got radial palsy."

We had not the heart to explain the explosive reaction. Instead we tried to persuade him that those shocked muscles would be so much better for the treatment. It was certainly not the physios' fault if they were not. Fortunately Dr Longsdale was an aspiring physician, for, had he had the responsibility of treating me surgically, I was loth to imagine the pain he might have expected me to endure.

Chapter 16

"ALL GLORY BE TO GOD ON HIGH"

Outside all was grey, and cold, and bleak; but inside there was light, warmth, and excitement. Christmas was coming. Peter wrote to say that he was on his way back to England. He arrived laden with maps, sketches, books, and pictures.

"Where," I asked, "are the brunettes?"

"I left them behind. I didn't know how this climate would affect them."

Peter took me to the places he had visited and when Perez arrived, I introduced them, and the three of us set off on a tour of Italy. Peter's vivid word imagery, supplemented by his sketches, kept us enthralled. Sister screened us off and let us continue. As he left, after the first evening of his return, we agreed that it would be advisable if he came one night a week only. He was busy, and so was I, and we both knew that there would be no limit imposed on the length of time he stayed.

"But over Christmas and the New Year, Swan?"

"Won't you be away?"

"Only for a day or so in between."

"All right. Come when you like then, but don't let it be a burden to you, Peter."

His blue eyes flashed. "Look, my girl, if it was a burden I wouldn't come. As I told you before, I enjoy talking about myself—all clear?"

"Yes, all clear."

It was lovely to have him back again and to know that he would be with me for Christmas. I waved my hand at him as

182

he turned in the doorway to smile his adieu, and I considered calling him back to help me solve the problem of presents for the staff, but I let him go because it seemed too much to ask of anyone, much as I wanted to give some small token in appreciation of what they were all doing for me.

This feeling of receiving all, and giving nothing, was further aggravated by the mountain of unopened parcels under my bed. Jimmy's better half was standing in the corner, with an operating gown draped over her, to make room for the gifts that were arriving, by post from New Zealand, and by hand from my visitors and my friends within St Mary's. Perez took an inventory of them every night, but he refused to open any of them for me until Christmas Eve, except the one that I knew, from the customs declaration form, must contain what my parents had sent over for me to give to Sister Linden. This he did open and repack with a card, Christmas paper, and tinsel string, before tying it on the tree.

The tree was enormous, but as I watched the gradual accumulation of the material it was expected to hold, I began to fear that it would not be large enough.

Christmas in Alexandra ward had begun long before the actual day of celebration. For weeks the other patients relieved the tedium of their waking hours by preparing elaborate decorations. I could do little to help, because my left hand was too weak and my treatment kept me busy, but I enjoyed watching the ever-growing mass of ingenious baubles strewn over the central table. There were gargoyles, bon-bons, dolls dressed as fairies in hospital gauze, and milk-bottle tops moulded into myriads of silver bells, which were to be strung together to hang like silver stalactites from the branches of the Christmas tree. There were stars in their hundreds, coloured ones and silver ones, suspended on tinsel thread then hung from the ward ceiling. Frilly streamers were made from variegated crepe paper, and all the big central lamps were surrounded by a rucked skirt of holly-green and red. Cocoons of silver and gold and a gross of balloons, which had been presented by a patient and inflated by the simple expedient of syphoning a charge from the oxygen cylinder into them, festooned the ward, making it unrecognizable. Everyone became infested with the gaiety and rumbustiousness of it all. Holly was brought and scattered in abundance, its shining leaves and bright berries filling any gaps left by streamers, stars, balloons, and gee-gaws. The students made my Balkan beam into a holly bower. Over my head they suspended a twig of dirty grey-green with club-shaped leaves, and tiny white seed balls that were a murky, milk-white colour.

"What on earth is that stuff?" I enquired.

The student, who was standing on my locker tying the twig above me, looked down in amazement. "Don't you know—honestly?"

"No. I've never seen it before."

"It's mistletoe."

"Mistletoe! That! But it's so drab, so, so—insignificant."

I was disappointed. It had always looked so pretty and delicate painted on Christmas cards.

"And it has some significance, you know." There was laughter in the voice above me. "That's why I'm tying it here."

"It must have, because I am sure no one could get romantic at the mere sight of it." It looked exactly what it was—a parasite.

Everybody was busy. Students, doctors, nurses, and domestics, all cluttering the ward with the spangled creations of the patients. A lighting-effects man from a theatre and an ex-patient of Sister Linden's added to the brilliance by erecting a cordon of coloured lights along the walls and into the tree, which towered against the securely bolted top door of the ward. A decorated piano made its appearance.

On Christmas Eve Peter and Perez arrived, almost simultaneously, to start unpacking my presents. Their reactions to some of the more feminine of them attracted a crowd of spectators, and provoked much laughter. They sniffed at cakes of scented soap; dipped their fingers into talcum powder as if it were an obnoxious concoction of snuff; sprayed themselves with an assortment of perfume; draped their masculine shoulders in dainty, lacy bed-jackets; sampled anything that was edible; peered at all the books. Peter even blew his nose on one of the handkerchiefs. Into the midst of the unwrapping strode a porter to tell me that there was a huge box down-stairs for me, and to ask me what should be done with it.

"Would you bring it up, please?"

"But, miss, I can't manage it on my own—I said, it's huge."

I looked at Peter and Perez, who shrugged their shoulders in resignation and departed with the porter. They returned strug-gling. The box was certainly huge.

"Thanks awfully—quick, quick, Peter. Get it opened."

He looked at Perez. "I think we'll leave her guessing, old chap, till she stops bossing us about."

They both sat down on top of the box, with their backs towards me. Perez glanced over his shoulder briefly: "In case you don't know, we are deaf—stone deaf—both of us." Then they began speculating on what could be inside the box.

Sister came bustling up the ward with her wide smile. "Would you two care for a cup of tea? We have just made some in the kitchen."

I groaned inwardly. They both jumped to their feet and walked away without a backward glance. I could not see the box, but I knew it was there. Nor was I allowed to forget it, because everyone who passed by my bed questioned me as to its contents, thus rousing my curiosity to fever pitch.

"I say, you know, I think we really ought to open this box for Swan. How about it?" Peter produced a hammer from be-hind his back, and a very innocent, round-eyed look on his face.

For my benefit they made great labour of prising the top off the box, but eventually Perez straightened up, and put a book in my left hand. "That's a start anyway." He bent down again as I opened the cover of the book. A note fell out. While I glanced through it I could hear them rustling paper, and be-moaning the fact that they had ever met me.

"Wait a minute, you two. Here, read this."

They both looked up quickly, more at the tone of my voice than my words. Peter dived for my hand.

"Swan, what's the matter? You're crying."

"Read that."

Perez took the note and they bent their heads over it. It was from the High Commissioner for New Zealand, telling me that the book and fruit were my Christmas gifts from him and his wife, but that the remainder of the parcels were presents they had packed for me to distribute. They had thought that I should, perhaps, wish to give something to the patients and hospital staff. They had printed my name on all the cards, and I was to say the parcels came from me. Perez looked up.

"What a splendid couple they must be. New Zealand ought to be proud of them."

"New Zealand is."

It was a matter of minutes before the box was emptied, because the High Commissioner and his wife had done a thorough job. All the parcels were wrapped in Christmas paper, and tied attractively. They had been sorted into piles and labelled: sixteen for the men patients; sixteen for the women; twelve for the nursing staff; six for the doctors; one for Sister; and two spares.

Perez filched Sister's report book for a minute while he hastily copied the patients' names on the back of my temperature chart. Peter came back from examining the tree. "I don't know how we're going to find space for fifty odd parcels on that tree."

Perez swung round from my locker, where he was printing on the cards. "Well, they're going on the tree. I'm seeing to that. We'll make space."

When they had finished Perez rushed away to join the carol singers, who were assembling in the hall below. Lights were turned out, candles were lit, to throw their tenuous glow on the tips of stars, catching intermittently the colour of a streamer, a holly berry, a waving balloon. From afar off came the chorus of students' and nurses' voices. The singing increased in volume until the shadowy mass of the choir spilled into our ward. Their voices fell away to the strains of:

"All glory be to God on high,
And to the earth be peace;
Goodwill henceforth from Heav'n to man,
Begin and never cease."

"I'll be back tomorrow, Swan. Anything you want, specially?"

"Well." I hesitated. "Do you think you could bring me my photograph album out of my trunk, please? Then I can have my family round me, in some shape or form, over Christmas."

When he had gone I looked around the ward. We had a motley but, for the most part, merry crowd of patients. At the bottom, against the right-hand wall, was a rheumatoid with a funny spleen; next to her was a heart; then a recuperating case of pneumonia; and, lastly, a lady who had just managed to get her test meals over and a long length of rubber tubing pulled out of her stomach via her nose in time for Christmas day. She was very happy. At the top in the corner nearest the tree was Miss Toxicosis, a youngish patient, who nearly drove us all silly with her complaint, which we had been informed on very good authority (her own), and about a hundred times a day, was thyroid toxicosis. Perez told me that her agitated dithering, and ninety-to-the-dozen speech, was all part of her glandular disturbance.

Between us was some high blood pressure belonging to a jolly soul, who did not allow the possibility of an operation to spoil any of her immediate enjoyment. At the foot of my bed, and against the left-hand wall, was a rather woebegone ulcer. I suppose she was thinking of all the things she would not be able to stomach on the following day. Alongside her was an empty bed; next, a messy interior as yet unknown, and unnamed; then Mrs Feeny-Barb, and no one was more thankful than I that she was as far away as possible. She was another heart, and we called her Mrs Feeny-Barb because she never ceased prattling, from daylight till dark, about her "feeny-barbs". They were her pills. We knew what colour they were, how many she had, how often she had them, how she felt before she took them, how she felt after she took them; and someone, for a joke, asked her how she felt while she was taking them, so we knew exactly what it felt like to swallow. Perez explained that her "feeny-barbs" were phenobarbitones, which had a depressive action on the activity in her brain, but, if she thought at the same rate as she talked, I shudder to think what must have been going on in her brain when she was not taking "feeny barbs".

Christmas morning was one perpetual shout of greetings, accompanied by sizzlings from the ward kitchen. This was the only occasion in the year when the nurses cooked our breakfast.

After breakfast I caught Staff Nurse's eye and called her to me. "Nurse, they are going to put me on a trolley, aren't they, to take me round the hospital?"

"Yes."

"I wondered if you could put me in it now—if it's not too much trouble." I pointed to the twig hanging above my head. "I want to get out from under that."

Nurse laughed, then shrugged her shoulders. "Very well, then. But, I warn you, it's no use. They all carry pieces of mistletoe round in their waistcoat pockets and hold them over your head, if you don't happen to be under a piece at the right moment."

With Jimmy, and the frame, I was soon transferred from the planks to the trolley, and at ten o'clock we went to the head of the stairs on our floor. Opposite us were more patients, and tier upon tier above us, still more; some in wheel chairs, some, with rugs wrapped round them, standing against the banisters, or leaning on a nurse.

"Can June see, nurse?" It was Sister's voice calling somewhere down the corridor.

"Can you, June?"

"Not downstairs, nurse. I'm too flat." She bustled off in the direction of the voice, to reappear in a few minutes with two huge pillows, Sister, and another nurse.

"What——" I began.

Sister took the pillows. "It will take three of you to lift her, and be careful. We don't want to have an accident." My head and shoulders were raised out of Jimmy. "Ease her back." I felt soft pillows beneath me, hands turning my head sideways, and I could see below me.

"All right, June?"

Now I could look down into the huge open vestibule on the ground floor. It was a sea of moving faces; nurses, students, sisters, doctors, honoraries, and dignitaries. Chords struck on a piano stilled the sea, and a Christmas hymn rose from its depths, to fill a well of space that reached higher and higher to the big glass dome overtopping St Mary's. I wanted very much to join in that hymn, but there were too many people too close to me. More hymns, some carols, and speeches, during the last of which Matron was manœuvred under the large stone entrance to the main hall, where a trailer of mistletoe had been twined round a light bulb. At the conclusion of her speech a general dive was made in her direction. It was with no little surprise that I noticed the older doctors reach her first.

No one belonging to the hospital seemed to be spending Christmas at home. Night nurses forfeited their day's sleep, and students seemed to be everywhere, accompanied by friends or accomplices, laying traps for the unwary. The Medical Superintendent appeared with a demijohn of refreshment. There was a toast for Sister, a toast with Sister, a toast for Dr Timms, a toast with Dr Timms: there were ample excuses for toasts.

Lunch, or dinner—or better, a noon-day feast—was served with stupendous pomp. Dr Timms, arrayed in white chef's cap and operating gown, carved the turkey. As he attacked his quarry, with the nonchalant efficiency of Sherlock Holmes, I thought of the big man dissecting the bird in the orthopaedic ward. Turkey and stuffing, ham, roast lamb with mint sauce, brussels sprouts, roast potatoes—everything appeared on our plates. The contrast, in both quantity and quality, from the ordinary hospital fare brought a sparkle to our eyes, whatever the anticipated consequences. There was a ravenously indecent clanking of cutlery on plates, while the last crumbs were scraped into mouths: a silence then a burst of cheering, as Dr Timms stepped from the kitchen into the ward bearing a flaming pudding aloft. It was carried on a silver-plated salver, dripping alcoholic fire.

In no time Peter was at my side. He propped the photograph album on my chest, while I showed him the ones I wanted him to take out and stand on my locker, beside the presents and the cable which my mother and father had sent me. Sister came to greet him, then disappeared into the ward kitchen to return, in a trice, with three glasses sparkling to the brim. Peter raised his eyebrows in mock surprise.

"Not you too, Swan?"

"No," I said, "I never drink, but this is a special occasion."

Sister sank my glass tube in one lot of bubbles, and held it for me, while she sipped her own. We were interrupted by a loud trumpet-call heralding the arrival of the pantomimists.

The house doctors and the students had spent weeks, prior to Christmas day, writing and producing farces, solely to delight the patients and their visitors. They were riddled with riotous references to hospital life, which contributed largely to their enjoyment.

"Little Red Riding Hood" saw Perez, in a very short gym dress, frame-heel nylons, and a long golden wig, mincing up the ward, basket on arm, to the words (which he sang in a high falsetto):

> "Oh! What a dutiful morning,
> Oh! What a dutiful day,
> I'm gonna visit my grandma,
> Several miles away . . . etc."

In the woods he was accosted by four rabbits, clothed in fawn jersey cloth, who performed an intricate *ballet à terre*— mostly upside down—for six minutes. Grandma was an anaemic-looking doctor, wearing a shroud, and a sister's poke bonnet. He was reclining on a mortuary trolley. The wolf was dressed as a "spiv"; broad of shoulder, flashy of tie, with painted tan shoes, and rakish hat. In a most effective baritone his wolfish cries made Grandma shudder in her shroud and enticed the inquisitive Riding Hood from the gambols of the rabbits. The ending was not conventional, for Little Red Perez was wooed, and won, by the wolf. Locked in each other's arms they disappeared out of the ward door. Grandma went with them but, somehow, she had managed to tie herself to the bottom of the trolley, and was hauled to the underworld with her back almost scraping the polish off the floor.

"The Boobs in the Ward" (with apologies to "Babes in the Wood") almost lifted the patients from their sick beds. It commenced with a forest dance, performed by doctors in slightly inebriated condition, wearing Peter Pan suits of camouflage green: there were three male trees, and one female. "Les dances des arbres" was a whirl of tipsy branches; arms and legs were everywhere at once, the male trees raised the female aloft to form a pyramid of greens for one static moment, then they were off again, cavorting, frolicking, high-stepping, until they dropped to the floor in exhaustion. The boobs entered, coyly, to take shelter under the comforting arms of the trees. One was Dr. Abbott, over six feet in height, wearing a sailor's shirt and short pants. His comrade was a mere five feet of cream tennis flannels. They were both sucking some thick white tack from bottles they were holding. The bottles got the biggest laugh of all. They were sterilized glass urine bottles, and from the tops of them projected long pieces of rubber tubing through which the white concoction was sucked. The usual purpose served by these pieces of tubing is known to most hospital inmates.

There was nothing tepid or half-hearted about Christmas day. Pantomimists, patients, visitors, and hospital staff, ate, drank, laughed, talked, and banged crackers, while the ward danced in a shower of decorations, and balloons burst of their own accord. After the cake had been cut everyone gathered in front of the tree, while the doctors distributed the gifts.

I lay contentedly in Jimmy, thinking of all that had happened, and adding greatly to my enjoyment of the day in the mere recollection of it. I glanced across at the tree and noticed, with relief and no little surprise, that our thyroid toxicosis had survived the deluge and was sleeping.

Sister came to me the following morning. "Did you enjoy yourself, June?"

"Oh, yes, Sister. More than I can say." Then I remembered something. "Don't you eat nuts over here on Christmas day?"

She looked at me with a sort of amused indignation. "Why, I brought you some nuts, and offered them to you last night—all shelled and ready to eat, but your only response was a stupefied grunt. You didn't even open your eyes."

I could not remember Sister's evening visit, or the nuts, or the night. Soon after Sister had left me, Dr Longsdale came to make his morning salutations. His steps lagged, and he was looking very drawn and shadowy about the eyes. He looked enquiringly at the cylinder of oxygen standing beside my bed.

"Are you in need of this, June?"

"Good gracious no! It was left there after the balloon blowing. Why?"

He made no reply but walked over to the door, behind which the screens were kept, lifted two of them in his arms, and proceeded to place them around my bed.

"What's all this for?"

Tired eyes were raised to mine. "It's not for you—it's for me."

He fitted the mask to the cylinder, then to his face. He turned the tap, and took several long pulls of oxygen. I was nonplussed.

"Heart trouble, doctor?"

He turned off the gas and replaced the mask. "No—but I've got a beastly hangover, and this stuff revives one no end. Takes all the exhaustion and tiredness away." Dr Longsdale was very much brighter as he resumed his round.

The New Year arrived before the glory of Christmas had departed. Ward routine was uninterrupted, except for the usual greetings. I lay contemplating which of my book gifts I should read, when my physios entered. I was very surprised to see them.

"Why are you wearing your uniforms?" I said.

A pair of surprised eyes caught mine. "Why shouldn't we? We always wear them when we give patients treatment—you know that."

"But you didn't treat me on Christmas day."

"Christmas day was a holiday."

"So is New Year's day. At least, it is in New Zealand."

"Well, this is not New Zealand, and we do not observe New Year's day as a holiday."

I was astounded. New Year's day at home was a second, but no less glorious, Christmas, and a public holiday. In a letter to my parents that evening I wrote: "These poor creatures do not know what New Year's day is. I can't help thinking of the sunshine on the river, the warm welcome of the sand; everyone bathing by day, and songs on the beach at night round one of our driftwood fires. But we all worked so it was not too bad."

Even if we worked all day, there was revelry by night. Theatre Sister sent an invitation, and some henchmen, asking me if I would care to attend their New Year party in theatre. I was taken on a trolley, the students sat out dances with me, I was plied with food, there were more toasts, and I saw one of the resident anæsthetists playing the piano with all his fingers and both elbows.

Next Sunday morning two nurses were trundling the heavy chair-scales from bed to bed, when Staff Nurse came up the ward heading in my direction. She held a piece of paper in her hand, and she looked more troubled than I had ever seen her. She stopped close to my bed and stared at the floor.

"For goodness' sake, nurse, cheer up," I said. "You look as if you'd just received a life sentence, or something equivalent to it."

Then she did look at me, and I didn't like what I saw in her eyes.

"What is it?" I asked quickly.

"June, I'm sorry—but I've some bad news for you."

My mind bridged a fearsome gap of fourteen thousand miles. "From home?"

"Yes."

"Quick, nurse, tell me."

She evaded my eyes. "It's—it's your father."

"My father?"

"Here . . ." She pushed the piece of paper into my hand.

It was a cable, from my mother, asking the Sister in charge of Alexandra ward to tell me that my father had died suddenly.

My poor, dear mother: I felt sick, and lonely, and rather frightened.

Chapter 17

A MAN UNDER MY BED

———∿∿∿⊙∿∿∿———

Aporter, a probationer, a plaster bed, and a polio; all on the roof of St Mary's in mid-February to see London under snow. All I saw at first was space, for my eyes, accustomed to viewing what went on within four walls, had developed a limited vision that confined itself to details at short range. We were on the top of the main theatre, and I had never seen such vastness. I looked at the pro standing by my side: she had suddenly grown very small, and I noticed the goose pimples on her bluish wrist where her hands were exposed to gather her cape about her. The girl was freezing while I lay under warm blankets with hot-water bottles flanking Jimmy's side. I must look at the snow quickly.

Roof-tops joined together under a blanket of white. There were no black lines, no angles: it was a landscape of flowing white curves rolling away into a mist. A bird had left a little track of marks and a crumbling break in the snow-line over the guttering; the porter's pants flapped against his legs as he stamped his feet; the thick red blanket covering me was rich against the sparkle of white. But I must not linger. I took one last look. "Thanks very much, we'll go down now."

Neither of them protested or hesitated.

I was now able to recognize signs of recovery in my body long before there was any visible indication of them. I do not think I could have worked out my theory of "squiggles" had it not been for my growing acquaintance with my own anatomy. The physios helped me with it by day, alluding to every muscle and movement by its correct name, and Perez helped me at night. He lent me books and, in the midst of a conversation about the latest Britten opera, or the matrimonial possibilities of someone on the staff, he would suddenly pop an anatomical question at me and expect an immediate and correct answer. I described my "squiggles" to him so often that he vowed he could feel them himself, although he did not have polio. A squiggle inside one's body is not an easy thing to describe. It was a thread of feeling extremely difficult to grasp which ran between my brain and the muscle I was trying to operate, but never, when it first began, ran true or straight. There would be a tentative quivering cord that wobbled about inside my head, and an equally reluctant sensation wobbling from the muscle to meet it. Sometimes the gap between the tenuous paths could be joined in a matter of days, sometimes it took weeks; but, however long it took, it was something alive inside me, and I tried to hold onto it, because my whole future depended on it. It reminded me of the contorted wriggling of a worm trying to reach cover after it had been cut in half by a spade: a struggling body without a rudder to guide and help it. But I struggled while the physios guided, and as the squiggles increased a more meticulous and concentrated mental control was required to keep them separated yet active.

At the first sign of a squiggle I told my physios, and they endeavoured to reinforce and strengthen it by every means available to them. We said nothing until there was visible movement: then my physios reported it, and an excited group of people in long white coats would come to view it and assess its worth. They often chided me for my lack of excitement, but, after weeks of connecting internal patterns and working squiggles into something that could be seen, I was too tired; and I knew that there was a whole network of such systems waiting to be untangled. I was always wildly excited when I felt the first uncertain quiver that told me something was happening, and I enjoyed the battle, but once the movement came and I could see what I was doing, there was nothing but relief, because the remainder of the fight was now primarily physical.

To advance from mere squiggles to movement means very little in terms of recovery, because the question of whether that movement is going to become sufficiently strong to be of any use is still to be solved. Its solution lies in work. Both Dr

Timms and Mr Muir, while encouraging me to work, insisted also that I be kept mentally stimulated, and this apart from learning anatomy. They looked after my physical well-being and placed the responsibility of my mental stimulation in the hands of the students, who forthwith brought me books on anatomy in their arms, books on more questionable subjects in their pockets, and a wealth of fun in their particular type of harmless devilry.

One day in mid-March I heard steps coming up the ward, then a voice outside my screens. "May I come in, June?"

Both step and voice were familiar to me. "Yes, Doctor Hume."

He stepped inside, stared at me, then laughed. "I give up," he said, throwing his hands in the air and letting them slap to his sides. "If it's not some extraordinary addition to your bed, or some quite unexpected movement in your muscles, or something you've thought up—well, anyway, what is it now?"

"What is what?"

"You know what I mean." He waved his hand at the water-proofing lining Jimmy's head, and pushed between his sides around my neck and shoulders; a porringer lying on my chest; and a tumbler of water with a tube leading from it to my mouth. "What's the meaning of all this?"

"I am practising projectile spitting. I believe that, with practice, I shall be able to spit water out of my mouth at a slight angle and with sufficient force to land in that porringer."

"But why——"

"Because, Doctor Hume, I hope soon that my left hand will be strong enough to clean my own teeth and, when it is, I want to be able to do it without any help from the nurses, so I have to learn to spit out my tooth-cleaning water."

"But don't you have to spit even when the nurses clean your teeth?"

"Yes, but they lift my head out of Jimmy, and turn it to one side of my mouth."

"No head movement yet?"

"No, Doctor Hume."

"You don't sound worried about it."

"I'm not."

I was not worried any longer about my head because, for three days and three nights, I had felt the first faint squiggles in my neck and stomach as I tried to pull my head out of Jimmy, but it was no use talking about them. They were things I alone knew existed; I knew that it would be a long time before movement followed, and then we could only guess whether that movement would grow strong enough to allow me to support my head again.

Perez arrived after supper that evening with a notebook and a business-like air.

"Hallo," I said. "What's to do?"

He went over to the central table, opened the drawer in the end of it, pulled out a bulk of notes, and came back to me with them. "I ought to find out all there is to know about polio from your case history." He dropped them on my locker. "I've got my finals in June, and I suppose I'd better know something."

"What rot, Perez. You know more than enough."

"That's what you think, my girl—hallo, what's this?" He unhooked my temperature chart.

"What?"

"This." He pointed to the name printed on the new page that had been put up that morning. All it stated, was: "Swan".

"Why?"

"Long neck, sloping shoulders."

He came closer and peered at me. "Well, your shoulders don't slope any more."

I was amazed. "Don't they really, Perez? They always used to."

"I think it's probably because your breathing was shallow when Jimmy was made and you had to pull up your shoulders to keep it going so, of course, the plaster set with your shoulders in that position, and has kept them there . . . but that's only my theory."

"I'm quite grateful anyway. I hope they stay there. I used to look like a bottle."

He grinned at me. "Supposed to be a sign of great beauty in Edwardian times."

He pulled a chair up to the locker and settled down to reading my case history, while I went on with some excavations that the author of the book I was reading was making in Athens.

There was a sudden, long-drawn-out whistle.

"What's up?"

Perez glanced at me and shook his head. "You . . . I just can't make out why you didn't die."

"Oh, for goodness' sake, don't *you* start that."

"But I had no idea. You see, I never actually saw you when you were first ill, and now when I read this"—he was holding a sheet of my notes in his hand—"it beats me."

"What's on it?"

"A report of your active movements at one stage of the game."

"And what were they?"

"It's not plural, my girl—it's singular. You could open one eye, that's all."

"Oh, dash it all. I think that's a bit far-fetched."

"What? A medical report? Not on your life. This is plain honest fact—no embroidery. What can you line up against that solitary eye in the way of movement now?"

"At the moment, I can use both eyes, talk, swallow, laugh, sneeze, blow my nose. I can move all the fingers on both hands but the right ones aren't up to much yet, use my left hand for some things, my left arm is moving but I can't lift all of it at once. I can breathe, I can arch my back just enough to make a small hollow between Jimmy and me, I can urinate and evacuate, and I can raise my right knee so that the back of it clears Jimmy by about two inches. . . . I think that's the lot."

"Any more brain-waves lately?" That was what he called my squiggles, and he was probably quite near the truth.

"Well, it's my head this time."

His hand gripped mine. "Splendid . . . do you know what that means?"

"Yes, Doctor Timms told me ages ago how important it was."

"Have you told him?"

"No. I want to leave it, Perez, until there's something definite for him to see."

"I understand."

He scribbled in silence for some time, while I went on reading.

"Were you badly frightened?"

"I never knew what fear was until I had this. It ran away with me, and I'd ~ever not been able to control fear before."

"But it's gone now, hasn't it?"

"Yes. I get a bit bewildered occasionally, but it's a sort of amused bewilderment. I don't think I'll ever be afraid again—not like that."

The main lights in the ward were switched off. I was completely immersed in my book when I heard a quiet voice close to me. "Where are you?"

"Excavating in Athens."

"Look at this." In front of me was a sheet of paper with a double red line ruled right round the edges of it.

"What's all that about?"

"The day you asked if arrangements could be made for you to do your own reading. Andrew Black must have been quite het-up to have gone to the trouble of putting these lines all round it."

"I don't see anything extraordinary in wanting to read—lung, or no lung."

"He seems to think there was. You know, it's been your safety valve—your reading, I mean. You're one of those fortunate people who can lose themselves in a book."

"If I've got a good book, yes. But that's what books are for."

He went back to his notes, and I turned once more to my reading. My case history had, by now, assumed formidable proportions and, as Perez seemed determined to plough through all of it, he was still bent intently over it when I heard a low murmur of voices at the end of the ward.

"Night Sister," I hissed.

He carefully folded the notes together, set his chair back noiselessly, then in one quick dive took all evidence of his work and himself under my bed.

"How are you, June?" whispered Night Sister.

"Grand, thank you, Sister."

"Don't read too late."

"No, Sister."

She turned to go, hesitated, and came back again. "What was that clatter I heard, up here, a short while ago?"

"Oh—um—actually, Sister, I think it must have been the window. It always does that when the wind's in a certain quarter."

She turned to Nurse. "Put a wedge in it, nurse."

"Yes, Sister."

"Good night, June."

"Good night, Sister." A few light steps and I heard the top door of the ward swing shut. "They've gone," I called in a loud whisper.

There was a series of bumps, some mumbled oaths, but no Perez. I wondered what had happened to him. A great deal of slithering and some thuds told me he was still under the bed. I heard Nurse coming up the ward.

"What goes on?" she whispered, as she opened the screens.

My stomach was aching with laughter that had to be silenced. "Nurse, there's a man under my bed."

"A what——!"

"Nurse——" It was an urgent whispered appeal from beneath us. "Please steady this confounded cast for me."

Nurse's eyes grew round. "Mr Casado?"

"Yes."

She bent down hastily and, after a short underground scuffle, straightened up with Perez by her side. He was dusting his sports coat and trousers.

"Oh, yes—you can laugh! I swooped under there and flopped straight into your precious Jimmy's better half. My feet slipped on the polish, and I just had to stay where I landed."

"Couldn't you have rolled out?" I asked.

His eyebrows shot up in indignation. "Roll? Every time I got a decent roll on it just rolled back again, and took me with it. However you manage to fit in that thing is beyond me."

"But then I don't try to lie in it sideways, or back to front, or head to heel."

He grinned. "No, I guess not. . . . I'd better leave before anything else happens." He turned to Nurse. "Don't forget to put a wedge in that window."

Next morning I was lying in Jimmy's better half with one ear buried in a mattress, which had been placed on the planks underneath us while the physios worked on my back. I heard footsteps advancing up the ward as a blanket was pulled hastily over my legs and seat.

"Who is it?" I asked.

"Sh . . ."

The screens scraped across the floor, and a rich cultured voice bade me good morning.

"Good morning, Mr Muir."

I felt a firm hand placed across the small of my back. "Try and raise your shoulders out of the cast."

He examined my back in detail and, when he had finished, there was silence all round me. After a while his hand was on my shoulder. "June, how would you like to go away from St Mary's?"

I did not like, not the least little bit, so I said nothing.

"You would like a change, wouldn't you, June?" It was Sister Linden's voice this time. After a pause in which I swallowed hard but still said nothing, she spoke again. "Why don't you answer?"

"I can't see anyone's face." If I could, I thought, I might get a better idea of what all this portended. Hands turned my face towards my locker.

"Can you see me now?" A face peered into mine.

"Yes, thank you," I said, thinking that those peaked eyebrows looked even more remarkable at such close range.

"Very well. Now, I want to send you away from here to another hospital. It's in the country. Won't you like that?"

"I'll go—if you want me to."

His face disappeared. "She sounds most dubious, Sister, and here were we imagining that she would be overjoyed at the opportunity."

"How soon do I have to go?" I asked in a tight voice.

Sister's face came into view. "Why are you so upset about it, June?"

"I don't want to leave here—that's why. I don't know what I'll do without all of you."

Then she laughed. "But, you silly old thing, you will be coming back to us. It's only for a few days."

"Well——" My relief was overwhelming. "In that case, please, somebody, tell Mr Muir I shall be very pleased to go, and shall enjoy it all tremendously, and thanks very much, and what am I going for, or can't I ask, or is it just a holiday, and how far away is it anyway, and who's coming on the journey with me?"

But the big man was still there, because his laughter joined that of the physios and Sister Linden before his face bent over the locker.

"Sorry, you misunderstood us. You will probably go in three or four weeks. You have to be measured for a spinal brace and some callipers. We don't do any of that here."

"You mean things to help me walk again?"

"Yes, but don't run away with the idea that you will be walking next week, or next month. These instruments take months to make, as they are all moulded by hand, but I want to get yours under way. Even after you have been measured it will probably be six months before you have a fitting."

Four weeks passed before Sister came to tell me that I should be leaving St Mary's, in three days, to take my trip into the country. One thing I did not have to worry about was what I should take, or what I should wear.

Perez came in the night before I left. "So you're running out on us?"

I grinned. "Running is right. Keep yourself in order while I am away, won't you?"

"Shan't have a chance. Sister Linden will be in charge of me." He shrugged slightly.

"Why, Perez? Do you have to go into quod again?"

"Yes. Second bed inside the door of George Bird in the morning. I've started to swell again. Look at my face."

I was studying him intently when a slightly puffy lid dropped over one of his brown eyes, shutting off the light and laughter in it for a split second: then it was released, as an expressive eyebrow was raised, and an amused voice asked me if I had done gazing. I felt myself smiling, and thought that nobody but Perez could manage to make other people laugh about something that was no laughing matter. And, always, he was fully aware of the uncertainty of his own future.

"What about your finals?"

"I'll carry on with my swotting in bed. I might even find time to drop you a note."

"If you do it will be answered in kind."

"Will it indeed? Even to any protestations I may make in it?"

"Yes. In fact, I'll add embellishments."

"Good. I think I'll write tomorrow."

Chapter 18

A COUNTRY INTERLUDE

—————∿∿∿⊙∿∿∿—————

Awet slant of drizzle blurred the large square windows
of the ambulance as it took me through London the
following morning. Jimmy and I, despite our horizontal position, could see as much as we wished of the outside
world. Of our chaperone, who was seated against the window
opposite, we saw nothing. I could not turn my eyes towards
her because they could not be drawn from the sights, now
familiar, and now strange, that appeared through our glass
screen as the ambulance took a slow, circuitous route through
the city. Apparently this was to be a sight-seeing tour, as well
as a journey towards measurements, and the country.

The people in the streets resembled the rain somewhat,
slanted moving bodies hurrying along in greyness; the buildings had an air of antiquity and solidity which one does not
find in New Zealand. On a stand in one window was a large
glass fish bowl. I thought of the fish inside it, then of my own
face framed in its piece of glass, and a bubble of laughter
caught me as I pictured, first the fish weaving a graceful pattern of iridescent beauty even in captivity: then myself, who
could lay no claims either to beauty, or to the merest suggestion
of a waggle in my tail.

We stopped at an intersection, and a truck, with two men in
the cab and a load of coal on the back, pulled alongside. The
man nearest my window looked across, and we smiled at each
other. The next time the ambulance had to stop, the truck
stopped with us. Again an interchange of smiles, but there was
amusement in them this time. The third time it happened I
laughed aloud, and waved my hand. The man on the near side
tapped the driver on the shoulder, spoke to him, then pointed

at me. I waved again: they doffed their coal-grimed caps, gave me a "thumbs up" sign, and we shot forward.

I heard a voice at my side: "Do you know those men?"

"Good gracious, no!"

"Oh, I thought you must."

"No, but they had kind faces, didn't they? Rather like London itself."

There was a chuckle. "They were pretty dirty faces."

"Yes—like London."

Gradually we left the vastness of London, and I saw the English country-side for the first time. Raindrops hung in the hedges, sparrows pecked busily at the damp earth, and a brindle cow lifted her head from grazing as we passed. Pansy eyes, placid and round, looking at nothing in particular: then, untroubled and unhurried, she moved away across a green space. Fine wisps of mist clung in the valley, and I thought of the tang of freshness that must be rising everywhere. We coasted up a long, wide avenue bordered by spindly trees: then we stopped.

Somehow hospital porters did not fit happily into an English rural scene, but I had been lucky: I had seen a cow. It was cold, and wet, and a little dreary, as they heaved Jimmy and me out of the ambulance onto a trolley, and buckled a large piece of waterproofing over us. There was a number of long, low buildings in front of us, what looked like a market garden and a poultry farm on a hillside to my right, and a stretch of woodlands to my left. There was a lot of air, of a bracing, unpolluted quality such as I had never known in London. I opened my mouth, the better to gulp it down, and had a smelly piece of rubber pulled over my head, my eyes, my nose, my mouth and chin. Two shafts of light running up either side of my nose pierced the darkness, but nothing could overcome the smell.

"What's this for?"

A voice came from behind me. "To keep the rain off."

"But please—I'd rather get wet."

"Maybe—but what about this here plaster head?"

I never knew where I went until the rubber proofing was removed, and I found myself being trundled along a narrow, wooden corridor, through a doorway, to stop with my feet and legs inside a long low wooden ward.

"Here's yer London polio, Sister."

I had never been called that before.

"Put her in the empty bed." A voice, but nothing that I could see. "What's she in—a cast?"

"Yes, and a frame."

"Well, you will have to remove the mattress, and put fracture boards on the bed."

I was taken halfway down the ward, and, after a considerable wait, lifted from the trolley onto a bed. My chaperone left with the porters, and I stared up at the ceiling, wondering why it looked so odd. Then I realized that there was no Balkan beam towering above me. From the number of beds I could see I guessed there must be at least thirty patients in the ward. Everywhere I looked there were eyes looking at me: I felt cold, and hungry, and a bit lonely.

"Have you been ill very long?"

It was a gentle voice that brought my glance swiftly to the left of me, where I saw a thin, pale face, under grey waving hair.

"A year."

"Oh, my dear—not a whole year with polio, and still in a plaster bed?"

That made me angry, but I had to behave myself. "It's not as bad as it seems, really it's not. I'm making a wonderful recovery. Look at my hand." I waggled my fingers at her and, to my horror, saw tears rolling down her cheeks.

"What have I said? I'm awfully sorry."

"I'm sorry I'm like this, but, you see, both my hands and arms are paralysed—nothing moves at all, and I'm afraid I am too old, and too tired, to fight."

"You! paralysed!" It seemed incredible. "But you can't have polio."

"I have—at the age of fifty-seven, and it's a disease that only the young can struggle with."

"How long have you had it?"

"Nearly five months."

I did some hasty reckoning. "You'll be all right. Quite all right. Your hands will come back—but give them time."

"Do you think so?"

"I'm sure of it."

I told her what I could of my own recovery, as far as my hands were concerned, but I saw that the hope it gave would not last. She had been right. She could not fight, because it was something she had never had to do in her youth, and now she was too old and too tired to learn, and her body lacked the recuperative power of the young. She would yield; but one could not condemn her for it.

At tea-time I wanted to hide my hand as it lifted the slices of bread and butter from a saucer on my chest, and took them towards my mouth. After tea a nurse came, and helped her out of bed; she could walk, but she could not brush her hair out of her eyes or her tears from her cheeks. She could not hold a handkerchief to her nose, or feed herself, or go to the toilet alone. I thought of the big man: I had grown older and wiser in one afternoon, and I moved my fingers slowly, one by one, in grateful acknowledgement.

During the days that followed I watched attentively while a young teen-ager opposite manipulated her callipers. I watched her put them on, and take them off, and I followed her dragging limbs as she creaked up the ward with the aid of crutches. There was nothing of grace or beauty in her movements, but they were movements, and the more I could learn from her the more able I should be to cope with my own instruments. One afternoon she brought her harness to my bedside in a wheel chair, and showed me how she fixed the steel shafts into the heels of her shoes, how she locked and unlocked the knee hinges, and how she laced the leather supports round her legs. Callipers could be easily mismanaged, and I realized that any paralysed person would need much practice in putting them on, apart from learning to walk in them. She did not have a spinal brace, but she had a vague idea that it was attached to the outside shafts of the callipers.

Seven days after I left St Mary's I was still on holiday in the country, I had still to be measured, and I was still receiving no treatment: but I had learnt that the quickest way to get things attended to at times is to keep quiet about them, so I said nothing, and concentrated on watching the girl with the callipers, and in lifting my head out of Jimmy. I was able to launch a concentrated attack on my head and was rewarded by an increasingly strong pull of muscles, and a lessening of the mental effort. I wondered how much a human head weighed as I gradually began to take more of the weight of my own.

But on the seventh morning of my rural interlude I felt my head drop a fraction through space as I released my straining stomach muscles. My face was hot, my hands shaking, as a wave of excitement burst inside me, but it had to be caught and held until I could be sure. I rested awhile, then shut my eyes and concentrated all the thought and strength I had in raising my head. Again there was that drop through space as I let go. A choking feeling of strain was all that I knew as I tried to raise it: no thought could be spared to wonder whether it was lifting or not, but that unmistakable movement of a weight, dropping through a gap onto solid plaster, was proof that I could take the weight of my head, if only for a second.

Pride struggled with tears: I wanted to send a telegram to St Mary's. I was fully aware that this was only a beginning: to take the weight of my head did not mean that I could control it, but it meant that control would come. There were months of inactivity to be accounted for, but the worst was over. Nothing like this had ever happened to anyone before, and it would never happen again, or so I thought until I became conscious of someone standing by my bed. I opened my eyes, found everything was as before, and could not refrain from grinning at myself for being such an egoistic dupe.

I was looking at two tall young men wearing white smocks, buttoned at the neck below the left ear and across the left shoulder, down the left side, and belted in round the waist. One of the men was fair, the other dark, and they both looked as if they were professional weight lifters. The smocks were short-sleeved, and two pairs of long muscular arms were carefully rolling my bedclothes off me. The fair one turned and met my astonished gaze.

"Hasn't anyone told you where you're going?"

"No."

"You're going for a swim."

"A SWIM! You must be crazy—no, I'm awfully sorry, you can't be." They were both smiling delightedly. "But, surely, you can't mean a swim, in water?"

"In water. What else do you think you'd swim in?"

The dark man was arranging some pillows in a long wicker spinal carriage. "Perhaps," he said, "she fancies a swim in milk —you know, like the film stars. Right now we're concerned with getting you out of this cast and dropping you into that spinal carriage. What usually happens?"

"You just grab what you can, when you can, and trust to luck. The only thing you'll have to watch is my head."

The fair one groaned. "Not one of those wobbling head cases?"

"'Fraid so."

"Well, don't you worry—we'll manage."

Somehow they did; quickly, and without hurting me. I lay on a soft mattress, with two hot-water bottles tucked against my sides, and masses of warm blankets over me.

We left the wooden building to cross a patch of green that took us to a path skirting the edge of the woods I had glimpsed on arrival. The orderlies went slowly, allowing me as much time with beauty as they dared, before taking me down a grassy rise and in through the big doors of a clean brick building, that was warm, and full of laughter. They stopped at the entrance of the pool room. I saw an L-shaped swimming-pool, blue water lapping, steam rising, eight people splashing about: then someone in a white uniform came towards us.

"Is this the polio from London?"

"Yes, Miss Tregarth."

She had warm smiling eyes and a flawless complexion. "How bad is this head of yours?"

"I can just take its weight, and only for a second at a time."

She looked at the two orderlies. "Will you stand by, please. We may need help."

I was wheeled into a small cubicle, then lifted onto a plinth with a rubber mattress on it. The orderlies were replaced by a young physiotherapist and Miss Tregarth who, I gathered, was the head of the department. They pulled a curtain, shutting off the pool, then began putting me into a bathing suit. They struggled.

"I used to have a rag doll once," I remarked casually. "I called it Floppy Fifi—I was very fond of it."

"Did you ever try putting a swim suit on it?"

"No. I can't say I did."

"And if you had, would it have mattered if you'd pulled one of its legs off in the procedure, or twisted its head round back to front?"

"No—there was always a needle and thread, and if the stuffing came out it could be poked back again."

"Exactly." They were laughing, and still struggling, for they had only got as far as my hips: but they won in the end. It was fun to be in a bathing suit again.

They put me on a strip of canvas, stretched tightly across a steel frame, that stood about eighteen inches from the floor. The orderlies carried me to the side of the pool and, with Miss Tregarth holding my head, they lowered me, still on the canvas, into the warm soft water. For the first time in my life I knew what it was like to sink. My body would not stay on that strip of canvas; nor would it stay on the top of the water. I could not even keep my head above water: Miss Tregarth did that for me, while my body tried to make a corkscrew of my neck. I was quickly lifted out of the pool. I think we were all relieved.

"I'm sorry, my dear, but it's too risky. You understand that, don't you?"

"Yes, of course, Miss Tregarth . . . and don't apologize. It was lovely to feel the water, even for that brief time. Why did I keep twisting round to one side like that?"

"I don't know your case well enough to be able to explain that. And, anyway, there's a great deal about polio that can't be explained. We have just got to accept the fact that, for the present, the extent of your paralysis makes the pool a danger."

I was stripped, dried, put back in my basket, and lay watching the swimming until lunchtime. As the orderlies began to wheel me away, smiling eyes looked down at me.

"Would you like to come over and watch tomorrow?"

"Yes, please."

That afternoon I had a letter from Peter saying he had been to St Mary's, expecting to find me back. He asked if I would write and tell him how long I was going to be absent, because no one seemed to know. Neither did I, but I wondered. And the following day when I returned with Jimmy from the physiotherapy department my wonder changed to apprehension as I saw a Balkan beam rearing its ugly head over my bed. It had an air of permanency. I asked no questions, ate my lunch, and thought a great deal. Suddenly the orderlies were by my side, with the spinal carriage.

"I'm not going out again?"

"You are," the fair one said.

"But there must be some reason other than pleasure this time. I've only just come back."

"Orders from Miss Tregarth. Somebody important wants to see you and we've got to be quick." They lifted Jimmy and me into the basket. As we went through the big doors and down the passage past the pool room towards the massage department, I laughed with delight.

"I know who wants to see me," I said.

"Who?"

"Mr Muir."

"The orthopod?"

"Yes."

The dark orderly looked down at me. "Don't get too excited, because I think you've missed your guess. He's not due here yet, and he never comes on a Wednesday. What makes you think it's him?"

"Can't you smell cigar smoke?"

They both held their heads up and sniffed, then burst out laughing. "By Jove, you're right."

They lifted me out of Jimmy, laid me on a warm rubber mattress in a curtained-off cubicle, and put a heating cradle over my legs. I heard a tramp of feet, and a deep, familiar voice. The curtains were pushed aside.

"Well, June?"

I couldn't stop smiling. "Hallo, Mr Muir. I can lift my head."

He took one stride in my direction. "Show me."

I was lying flat on the rubber mattress, without a pillow. I shut my eyes and heaved. My head seemed to spring up like a Jack-in-a-box, and it had a long drop back onto the mattress. I opened my eyes in astonishment. "It's never done that before," I said. "I could only lift it the merest fraction. I can't believe it."

The big man was smiling. "I don't want to minimize the importance of this, because it is important, but your head is lying on rubber at the moment—not in a plaster cast. Would you do it again please?"

He drove the tips of his fingers into my stomach and, as my head shot upwards, I could feel the weak belt of muscles striking something firm.

"That plaster cast has been the best thing for you to practise this in because it couldn't give you any assistance. You are taking the full weight of your head on your own. That is excellent."

"How far can I raise it, Mr Muir?"

"A full inch I should say, on this," as he patted the rubber.

"An inch? Oh, no! It feels like ten or twelve to me."

He smiled. "I have no doubt it does. But don't be discouraged—you know how important it is. You concentrate on getting a shrug into your shoulders, and then I can start to talk about letting you sit up."

He began to examine my legs and back. I lay wondering what the big man had really come for. I did not think that it was solely to examine me.

He stood over me for a few seconds in silence, his hands in his pockets. "You are to be measured tomorrow, June, but you will be too tired to travel after it so you will return to St Mary's the following morning."

"Thank you, Mr Muir."

Early next morning Jimmy and I were lifted onto a trolley and were taken to the operating theatre where there was a group of unfamiliar faces, but all too familiar galoshes, rubber aprons, and long gowns. There was no plaster bath, and there were no strips of gauze. Theatre Sister introduced me to the instrument maker.

"Can you sit up?" he asked.

"No, I'm sorry, I can't."

"Haven't you been sat up at all, since your illness?"

"No, not once."

"Well, we have got to have you sitting up to make this spinal cast."

I was lifted out of Jimmy and placed on a hard high bed; then a close-fitting stockinette jacket was pulled over my head and down my body. It was a squeeze, but it was infinitely better than being jellied. I was lifted from the bed, carried across the theatre, and held gingerly over a hard wooden plank, only a few inches in width. My feet were slowly lowered to the floor, and my body drawn up into a sitting position. My chin plopped onto my chest, and my head felt light.

"Watch her head."

Someone was kneeling down, holding my feet in position on the cold floor, while someone else held my knees firmly together. My right arm was lifted by one person; my left by another, and both were held straight out in front of my body at shoulder level. I did not envy my arm-holders their job. I had two more supporters one on either side of me pushing against my body to try and prevent me from slipping sideways. With the instrument maker steadying my back with one arm, and someone holding my head, we totalled nine: I was the only one who was not doing anything to keep myself straight.

"She still sags," said Mr Kyte.

Even Floppy Fifi, I thought, was never as disobliging as this. A triangular canvas sling, with a halter attached to it, was lowered from the ceiling. It was fitted under my armpits, around my chin, and the back of my head.

"Right!"

Hands left my head, the halter tightened, I felt myself being pulled ceiling-wards and wondered how it was I managed to stay on the plank.

"Stop." It was rapped out. "Fix her at that, please, she's good and straight now. Keep her steady, I'm starting."

This time I was being bound in plaster. A cold wetness passed round and round my body. The cold was intense, and peculiar things were happening to me. The abrupt change, from a horizontal position to a right-angled vertical one, was jangling little bells inside my head, and causing the wall opposite me to loom large before me, then recede, loom large, then recede, like a wave on the sea shore. There was a blur of white, and a voice from a distance.

"How are you feeling?"

The strain on the halter clamped my teeth together. "Can't . . . see you."

"Shan't be much longer, lass."

Something trickled inside my bottom lip. "Try and get that down. Suck your breath in hard, and swallow." It was very bitter. "Did you get it?"

"Mm."

I was given some more, and gradually the wall opposite settled into place and stayed there, and I became aware of what was taking place around me. There were pins and needles in my arms and hands; a doctor was taking my pulse; there were hands still wrapping me in coldness; and Theatre Sister standing to one side of me with a medicine glass in one hand, and a blade of steel in the other. At last there was a pause, followed by rapid smoothing movements all over the plaster.

"That will do. I'll get it off her as soon as possible." I had been so occupied, with my little bells and my blurry eyes, that it had not occurred to me to wonder how this mould would be parted from me. It had solidified into an immovable white mass round my torso, and there seemed no reasonable answer to the riddle of its removal.

"Thank you, Sister."

The steel blade changed hands and was pointed at my throat. Although my teeth were clenched I could still make a noise. I did. The blade paused in mid-air, and all eyes were upon me.

"Whatever is wrong?"

"I'll be cut open."

"Pull yourself together, lass. I've never cut anyone yet and I've done this hundreds of times."

I gulped. "Please . . . be careful."

He gave me a look that was both humorous and exasperated.

"Shut your eyes."

It was an order that brooked no denial. I heard a rasp of sound and felt a thin line of pressure moving straight down my centre front. The mould was eased carefully from my body and the hanging rope was released; I sagged into a bundle of arms and was lifted onto the high bed.

My return to a horizontal position reduced everything to normality. Mr Kyte was standing by a table mending the split he had made in my bodice with a long strip of plaster-impregnated bandage. He came over to me as he was giving it a final smooth.

"I'm very sorry for the commotion," I said, "but I still don't know how you managed to get that mould off me without cutting some part of me."

"Don't you remember this?" He held up a long piece of lead about an inch wide. It was like a flat yard stick.

"No," I said, "I don't."

"This was slipped underneath the stockinette, down the mid-line of your body, and the knife cuts into it."

Even with half an inch to spare on either side of the knife, I thought that it would not be difficult for the majority of people to veer off the protective edge of the stick in the downward course of the cutting, particularly as plaster requires strength in the hands that wield the blade, and the stick cannot be seen.

I remained in a horizontal position while casts of my legs were taken. When both legs had been plastered and cut free, Theatre Sister removed her gown and brought forward a basin of warm water. I was thoroughly scrubbed, then put back in Jimmy. Plaster patterned the floor with huge octopus-like splashes of white. Mr Kyte tucked my body under one arm, my

legs under the other, and tramped out. He paused in the doorway and glanced back.

"I've got to go into London with these. Not many men can
travel about safely with a dissected woman in their arms."

These were what is termed "negative" casts. The hollow
inside them is filled with more plaster, thus making a replica of
the patient's body and legs, or "positive" cast. When this has
set the instrument maker fashions the steel supports and brace
to fit exactly the contours of the person who is to wear them,
beating leather and bending heated steel on the actual mould.
The steel is hard and the leather tough to withstand the strain
of the dead weight of paralysed bodies and limbs. The work is
done by hand, and is a painstaking process. The final result
comes after months of ceaseless labour, but it is labour that
remains unapplauded. The thought, and the sight, of "irons"
or instruments makes people shudder, even those who have to
wear them; no thought is spared for the man behind the scenes,
the product of whose skill is greeted with looks of distaste and
foreboding. But there is a quiet pride in what they do, and the
satisfying knowledge that they put hundreds of otherwise
immobilized people on their feet; and that inner satisfaction is
of far more worth than loud-mouthed public acclaim.

Chapter 19

MISS POTT SITS AND
SO DO I

The morning after I had been measured I returned to St Mary's. I saw nothing of the country or London because the ambulance windows were of frosted glass; but I did not care. I was lifted out of the ambulance at the street entrance to Casualty department. Two porters walked down the slope towards us, one of them a tall, dark-haired, ruddy-faced Irishman who had wheeled me about many times.

"Well," he said, "look who's back . . . my dream girl." Then he turned to the ambulance driver. "All right, we'll take over. We know where she goes."

Through Casualty, out across the main hall, and into the lift.

"Hallo, Herbert."

"'Ullo, miss—'ave a nice time?"

"Yes, thank you."

A little, thin, smiling man, with stringy wisps of grey hair, Herbert the liftman was the most popular, yet the most abused, man in the hospital. Voices hailed and harangued him all day long and lights flashed above his head, but he was always smiling, always unruffled, and he never answered back. It paid him not to. His name was a cry of agony from the maids with the meal trolleys; a gentle beseeching interrogation from nurses; a short clipped command from some impatient doctor; an angry explosion, accompanied by a rattle of gates, from porters with X-ray and theatre patients; and all the time the beckoning wink of the lights. He was HerBert, HerButt, HerBitt, HerBett, and HerBee: and all these again without the aspirate. Sometimes a "hurry" was prefixed to the demand, but no one could hurry Herbert, because Herbert could not hurry the lift: behind those sliding iron doors he reigned supreme.

We shot upwards, stopped, the doors clanged open, a short stretch of corridor and in through the top door of Alex. Planks, Balkan beam, slings and springs, all in my corner of the ward, and on my locker a vaseful of sweet-scented stocks. Staff Nurse came up the ward with a wide smile.

"Hallo," she said, "here's trouble back again."

"Hallo, Sue." Matron was not about. "How nice you look —— How is Perez?"

The smile was gone. "He's very ill."

"Worse than he's been before?"

"Yes. He's wonderful, June. He's sitting up in bed with tubes in the soles of his feet draining fluid out of his body into two trays on the floor . . . and he's studying."

I heard the top door open and looked across the ward to see Sister Linden. "Hallo, Sister."

She crossed quickly to my bed. "Hallo, my dear—how are you?"

"Grand, thank you."

"Did you enjoy yourself?"

"No."

She looked somewhat taken aback. "Oh, come now—the fresh air and the lovely food——"

"One day, Sister, you will realize that people mean more to me than places."

She laughed. "I don't believe you. Now, what do you want? Lunch first, of course, and then a rest. I'll bring your mail back with me, there's such a pile for you."

"Thank you—and thank you also for the stocks."

She looked at me in quick surprise. "How did you know I put them there?"

I grinned. "I didn't. I only guessed, but now I do know."

"You're impossible."

"Sister, I can lift my head."

"I know. Doctor Timms told me."

"Who told him?"

"Mr Muir—and now, I must ring and see about some massage for you."

I lunched, gossiped, and read my mail. Among letters and food parcels there was a photograph of my sister which I propped up on my chest.

"Would you like that on your window ledge?" It was the patient in the bed next to mine.

"Yes, please. Are you allowed up?"

"Yes." She stood my sister beside my books. "She's lovely, isn't she? Not a bit like——" She clapped her hand to her mouth.

I laughed. "You may as well have finished it. Everyone that knows us says the same thing. She is lovely, and we are not a scrap alike."

Two physios suspended me, then lowered me onto a mattress. They turned a lamp on me, and massaged every square inch of my back, arms and legs. Late in the afternoon I dropped back into a smooth, powdered Jimmy. The stiffness taken out of me I was happy and at rest. Peter came in the evening bringing news of plays, opera, ballet, and a book of Paul Nash's paintings. I sent my love in a five-line limerick to Perez, and in less time than it took me to think up the first line of mine, Nurse was back with one from him. It sent us both into gales of laughter.

"He wants to see your sister's photo."

"Take it across please, nurse."

When she returned she was empty-handed.

"Where's my photograph?"

Nurse chuckled. "He's got it propped up on his locker, and he wants your home address."

In the form of an address I wrote down four of the longest Maori place-names I knew. They were all in different parts of New Zealand. "Tell him I'm going to sleep now, nurse, please."

As Nurse walked down the ward a strange figure in a white coat came towards me.

"You're June, aren't you? It's fairly obvious." His eyes swept upwards. "Sorry I couldn't get along to see you earlier. My name's Smale—I've replaced Clive Longsdale."

I sighed. "You're always changing. I no sooner get accustomed to one face than it disappears. No permanents—only Doctor Timms and Mr Muir and they aren't here all the time, which leaves Sister, Mrs Venning, and me. I say, excuse me, but would you mind turning your face sideways for a second?"

He grinned. "Which side do you want first? I look quite different depending from which side you view me."

He had curly light brown hair, grey eyes, and a pale skin. A pleasant face, not in any respect unusual until one caught the marked difference in it when viewed from opposite sides. It was not a difference in expression, but in actual facial contour.

There was a chuckle of laughter. "Finished?"

"Sorry, but it is odd, isn't it?"

"Yes, that's exactly what it is—odd. And now, if you've finished examining me, I'd like to get these notes up to date before tomorrow morning. Tell me, briefly, what happened that is of any value."

While he questioned me, and filled sheets of paper with a rapid scribble, I introduced him to my mother's biscuits. He paused to eat one.

He tapped his pen on Jimmy's frame. "Look, there's not much I can do for you—medically, I mean; but if you ever want anything in the way of books, or fruit, or telephone messages, or anything like that, don't hesitate to ask."

"Thanks very much, Doctor Smale. As a matter of fact, I want something done about my golf clubs, and my tennis racquet. Someone could be making use of them, and I'd like someone in St Mary's to have them. There are seven clubs—men's ones because I liked a long shaft, and both tennis and golf balls, although I don't know what they'll be like now. Don't think I'm throwing in the sponge, will you?"

Next morning the head of the physiotherapy department arrived with two physios I had not seen before.

"Miss Ainsworth, and Miss Tudehope," she said, indicating the girls in turn. "Miss Ainsworth is going to treat you all the time from now on. No more changing. And Miss Tudehope will help her suspend you. Mr Muir says that you can dispense with the anterior shell now, and be lowered onto a mattress every day instead. You are to have your midday meal out of your cast, but you mustn't sit up yet." She turned to Miss Ainsworth. "Get a piece of sponge rubber and fit it inside the cast, underneath June's head. Mr Muir says she can have a small pillow now."

When she had gone I was swung aloft, Jimmy and his frame were removed, and replaced by a mattress and under-sheets. At lunch time, when Betty Ainsworth removed the screens round me, I was lying in a bed like all the other patients. I was much nearer floor level, and my body felt very small in the seemingly limitless space of a normal bed.

In the middle of the afternoon my physio nodded towards Jimmy's better half propped against the wall. "That must be taken away. You won't be needing it any more, and it only adds to the clutter." She held my right hand in both of hers and made me move my fingers.

"Can you knit?" she asked.

I pulled a face. "I know how to."

"But you don't like it."

"It drives me silly. I loathe it."

"Well, I want you to try and do some."

"Oh, please," I begged, "I'll do anything else. Polish the silver, make swabs, anything. If you insist you'll have a raving lunatic on your hands."

"But knitting involves all the fine muscle movements of your fingers and hands."

"Isn't there any other occupation that involves them?"

She was about to reply when Dr Timms, Dr Hume, Dr Smale, and the ward students pushed inside the screens. One of the students leant against the wall and sent Jimmy's better half crashing to the floor. He picked her up with a grin as Sister came bustling to see what the noise was about. In answer to her question I pointed to the offending cast.

"That's what did it. I've no more use for her, Sister, and the physio suggests she is cremated."

"Oh—I'll take it out of the way and get the porters to dispose of it."

As she walked down the ward we could see the upper portion of the headless wonder clad in the top unit of her two-piece bathing costume. I wondered what the porters would do to destroy her for she would be solid, and unyielding, even to an axe.

Dr Timms and Dr Hume decided that I had to have something that they called an electro-cardiograph, so, next morning, I was taken up in the lift and wheeled into a dark room. Dr Hume was there: I could hear his footsteps as he moved about. He came close, rubbed some sweet-scented cream on me, and put little discs on the cream. The discs seemed to have long leads attached to them.

"Are you making a tape-recording of my heart?" I asked into the darkness.

There was an impatient smothered exclamation. "Why did you speak? I'll have to start again. And, please, be quiet this time."

I did not even open my mouth to apologize.

I had not been back in the ward long before Sister approached my bed, with her starched apron flapping round her hips, and the light of battle in her eyes. She was clutching a brown paper parcel. She stopped abruptly. She opened the parcel. It contained a ball of mustard-coloured wool, two knitting needles, and a pattern for woollen gloves in garter stitch. She spread them on my locker: then she looked at me.

"Supposing, Sister," I said very carefully, "supposing I can't knit."

She waved an impatient hand. "Of course you can. Now, do you, or do you not, want to strengthen those hands?"

"I do."

"Very well, you will start knitting." She put the wool, the needles, and the pattern on my chest.

I grinned at her. "Thanks very much for winding the skein into a ball for me. That was very thoughtful of you." I turned to my physio. "What made you——"

"Go to Sister? I was told before I started treating you that it was not much use arguing with you. The only answer was to go to Sister Linden, for whom all things——" She finished by

222

pointing at the loop I had tied and was trying to slip over the first needle. "Shall I cast on for you?"

"No, thanks. I've got to knit, so I knit—by myself."

I discovered I could cast on with one needle and my thumb, but my right hand pulled the stitches off the left-hand needle as I jerked hopefully into the mustard loops. What with speaking out of turn in the dark room, and my right hand insisting on undoing what my left had accomplished, my morning had not augured well. Staff Nurse and a junior whizzed from bed to bed on the after-lunch tidy up. They straightened the counterpane over my bed cradle, kicked Jimmy and his frame a bit further out of sight under the bed, and straightened the castors. Staff Nurse looked up.

"What's the matter? You're very quiet."

"I've got a pain in my side, and I think I'm going to vomit."

She sent the junior for a bowl, and she went for Sister. The junior was quick: she had me screened off, and was standing by my bed, when Sister came in with some white liquid in a medicine glass, and two tablets in a spoon. She was too late.

"Where is the pain?"

"In my left side. It's like a stitch, only worse—it comes in waves, and makes me shake."

"Get Doctor Smale, nurse."

"Yes, Sister."

She held the basin and took my pulse: the pain increased.

Dr Smale arrived and dug his hands into my side. "She's certainly tied up in knots. A hot-water bottle, Sister?"

"Nurse is bringing one."

"Good. I'll get Doctor Nairn—he's over on the other side."

Dr Nairn was the physician in charge of Alex. He came in with a smile. "Well, June—our acquaintance grows"—he went round the left side of my bed—"under the most unpleasant circumstances, I see."

He asked some questions, felt my side, and looked at Dr Smale. "You were right. It's renal colic. Give her an injection of morphia and atropine immediately, and if things haven't eased off in twenty minutes, give her another." Then he turned to me. "This is not surprising, because you have been supine for so long and your kidneys haven't had a chance to drain properly, but that doesn't make it any less painful. We shall rid you of it eventually, but, until we get it in hand, you will possibly get similar attacks. Never let the pain get as bad as this again. Tell Sister when you feel it coming on, and we'll give you something to stop it before it gets out of control."

I do not know what it was about me that made everyone greet my knitting activities with amused surprise. Their reactions had nothing to do with the fact that I had polio: I simply did not appear to them to be the sort of person who would knit.

The pattern began at the top of the thumb, and, when I reached the base of it, I had to put the stitches on a safety-pin and start at the top of the first finger. Using only two needles, I found myself with two flat pieces of knitting that had to be explained, so I searched the pattern until I found the clue for the corresponding pieces, knitted them, and sewed the two together. Thus I made a stall for my thumb, and another for my index finger, with safety-pins dangling at the base. I was careful to put these on before enquirers came too near the bed, because it was obvious then what they were. They would still have required some explaining had I not worn them. These two stalls occupied me for three weeks. Had I not done enough?

"No," came Sister's retort.

"How much more?"

Sister looked wildly about until her eyes lighted triumphantly on an orange on my locker. She picked it up. "When you can peel one of these you may stop knitting."

I made a stall for my middle finger, and a flat half piece for my third, before I was able to skin an orange. It took me the whole of a Sunday morning. I was glad to be occupied because it was impossible to read or think, with the constant babble that accompanied the passage of the scales round the ward. I wondered if the men spent a morning discussing their pounds avoirdupois. I determined that I would never weigh myself, or discuss my weight again, when I left hospital. The fat patients were always those who never ate anything, and couldn't understand why they were fat. They supposed it was glands. The thin ones were those who spoke of the enormous quantities of food they consumed, and couldn't understand why they weren't fat. They put it down to glands eventually, too. The fat ones shrugged superior, well-covered shoulders and let it be known that men appreciated curves. The thin ones hid wide smiles in bony faces, and tightened the belts of their dressing-gowns round slim waists.

I ate my orange slowly and wondered if I dared shoot the pips about. I carefully wrapped the peelings in a handkerchief for Sister's scrutiny. She was off duty.

Next morning as she made her ward round I was reading. "Why aren't you knitting?"

"Look—look, in there." I pointed to a paper bag on my locker. Sister pulled out some wizened pieces of peel. "I've peeled an orange, so that means an end to knitting, doesn't it?" I was triumphant.

Sister twinkled. "Your knitting may rest, but in future you will be sent every orange in the ward to peel."

Thirty-two patients; half a dozen oranges each a week; anything from twenty-five to thirty oranges per day, and it had taken me a morning to peel one. But it was infinitely preferable to knitting, and I welcomed the smell because it helped to stifle a more obnoxious odour which, at that time, clung to my body and my bed, and which was caused by the three-hourly doses of medicine I was taking to combat colic.

It had a vile smell, and a vile taste, and, as I had to take it for weeks on end, I exuded its vileness. It had a long name, which the nurses abbreviated to something that sounded to me like "Miss Pott Sit and Higher Sigh Miss". It was Latin, of course, because it was medicine, and when I wrote a note asking Perez what it was short for, he replied in good old English—but his reply is unprintable. It was a case of Miss Pott etcetera versus orange peel. The peel won in the day time: Miss Pott was victorious during the night.

My hands strengthened, and I could run my right fingers like crabs' legs over the bed, pulling my paralysed arm behind them. My head and back grew stronger, and a group of muscles in the upper half of my right leg. I had learnt my anatomy and one day, in front of Stephen's uncle, I expressed a desire to learn Chinese because the characters had always fascinated me. The following week I received two books on a basic 1400 characters, and a visit from two students attending the school of oriental languages, in London. I looked at one of the students in surprise because he was obviously from China. He was short, immaculate, and soft-spoken.

"Why are you studying Chinese?" I asked.

He smiled. "There are many different dialects. I know only my own. Just now I am studying Cantonese."

"And you are?"

"I am a Pekinese." His brown eyes were alight. "You may laugh—everyone does, but I do come from Peking."

Towards the end of July Mr Muir, after one of his periodic muscle tests, looked down at me, and said:

"Tomorrow, we shall sit you up, with a back rest and pillows, although I want you to keep erect by yourself if you can, if it's only for a moment. The pillows will be there for you to lean against when you tire." He looked across at Betty. "About ten-thirty tomorrow morning? You had better have help."

"Yes, Mr Muir."

Mrs Venning came to me as she was going off duty. "Sister tells me you'll be sittin' up in the mornin'. I'm comin' early. Can't miss you sittin' up, ducks, can I now? I'll bring you a nice hot cuppa before them-all comes."

In the morning one of the second-year nurses braided my hair and coiled it up on top of my head. She held a mirror while I shakily applied some make-up, then she and Betty rolled me about in my bed until they had put the green fuzzy bed-jacket on—the right way. I had always worn it back to front. Staff Nurse brought a back rest, and pillows enough for a dozen patients. Mrs Venning brought the promised cup of tea.

At half-past ten Betty stood close to the head of my bed on one side, Miss Tudehope on the other. Staff Nurse was ready to slip the back rest into position, and Sister the pillows. A junior stood close with a bowl and a cloth, held discreetly behind her back. Mr Muir, Mr Pastaad-Noyes, and the head of the physio department were framed in the Balkan beam at the foot of the bed, in a direct line with my body. Dr Timms about mid-way down on one side: Dr Hume facing him. Dr Smale, the ward students, and some of the physios who had treated me, stood where they could.

"Right." A deep voice from the foot of the bed.

Betty and Miss Tudehope raised me quickly, and there were brisk movements behind my back before I felt pillows propping me in position. The top half of my body felt suddenly light, my stomach fat and heavy, and there was a sudden pain in my shoulders. I felt high and awkward and everything about me was smaller. Dr Timms had his hand on one wrist, Dr Hume the other. No one spoke.

Through the silence, and the students, came a small scuffling figure in a white smock, to lean both hands on the edge of my bed and look up into my face. There were tears in Mrs Venning's eyes.

"Gawd, ducks," she said, "you look like that there queen what 'ad 'er 'ead chopped orf."

Silence for a split second, then a roar of sound that meant laughter from every throat. I put my left hand over my stomach to still its jelly-like quivering, because I knew that I should be too weak to do anything unless I could stem my mirth. The noise died away to a few stifled gusts.

"What's her pulse like?"

I looked at the foot of the bed. The big man was still smiling.

Dr Hume looked across at Dr Timms. "We'll have to start again," and as they put their hands on my wrists, "you will have to pay for this, June. It is quite a privilege."

I could maintain an erect posture only for a few minutes before my head and my body sagged to the right, but I did not faint, I was not ill, and I managed to push my right hand across a piece of paper to inform my mother that I was sitting up in bed. I sat for half an hour before excitement, and my changed position, forced me back to the horizontal. The future looked promising.

Chapter 20

SCURVY, A PISTOL SHOT, AND A BRIDGE CROSSED

———◆∿∿∿∿∿◍◆◍∿∿∿∿∿◆———

Next day I sat up in bed for lunch and I used a knife and fork, or rather, I held the knife, and used the fork. It was a long lift from my lap to my mouth, and my left arm protested. Dr Smale walked in the top door of the ward as my hand dropped for the third time to my plate, without leaving any food in my mouth.

"Struggling, June?"

"Yes. My arm will drop just before I take a mouthful, and I daren't bend my head to meet it."

"Give it a rest, then start again, and if you need help call a nurse."

I thanked him, but I could not see myself asking a nurse to feed me at this stage. He walked away and there was a voice beside me:

"June, there's someone at the door trying to attract your attention."

I looked over. Through the partly open door I could see a blue and brown paisley silk dressing-gown, and a pale face caught up in a wide grin. Face and body came further into the ward as the figure made a deep bow. I was tempted to repay it, but could see my face falling into my lunch if I bent forward from the waist, so I waved my hand at the closing door. At the same moment I heard the nurse, who was carrying meals on the men's side, telling Sister Linden that Mr Casado had disappeared.

"Disappeared, nurse! where could he disappear to?"

"I don't know, Sister, but he's not in his bed."

Sister dropped the custard ladle and sped quickly out of the bottom door. She was soon back. "What have you done with Mr Casado's sweet, nurse?"

"It's on my tray, Sister."

"Take it across to George Bird. Mr Casado is in the second bed inside the door." As if poor Nurse did not know which bed he was supposed to be in.

Four days later I was out on the balcony in the sun looking at the plane tree. I had avoided the Sunday morning weighing-in, and lay listening to the organist practising a Bach voluntary in the hospital chapel.

There was a quiet voice by my side. "What—no singing?"

"Ah! Congratulations, Doctor Casado."

"Thanks. How did you know?"

"Sister told me last night. I hoped I'd see you today. I'm so pleased, Perez. What are you going to do now?"

"I've got to get out of George Bird first, of course, then I think I'll try some research at the Institute of Bacteriology."

"Here, in St Mary's?"

"Yes." He gave a rueful grin. "They can keep an eye on me here . . . grand to see you sitting up the other day. No spinal carriage, now. From the look of your back when you were sitting up the great Muir has something to be proud of."

"It's *my* back!"

He nodded. "I grant you—but it was Muir's to make or mar."

"I know, Perez. I'm just a bit tired of being so grateful, so often, and for so long. Whenever I've tried to thank anyone, they shrug it aside and walk away."

"They're human; they like praise. They are a trifle embarrassed, but still they like it." He was pacing up and down the balcony. "Here comes Tony Smale—wonder what he wants."

Dr Smale looked hot and tired. He dropped into a chair, put his feet on the balcony rail, and drew out a packet of cigarettes. "What wouldn't I give for a nice, long beer!"

Perez pulled up another chair. "You on call in Cas today?"

"Yes, and the place is like an inferno. Five admittances in the last hour, and on a Sunday. Why do people have to make a mess of their week-ends? Not enough sense to get ill during working hours, I suppose. It would pay them better."

"Why don't you remove your coat, Doctor Smale, and cool off?"

Dr Smale grinned, threw his white coat over the corner of the trolley, and rolled up his shirt-sleeves. "By the way, Perez, know anything about a Hungarian heart case—been in Alex before, I understand?"

"Mrs Manning?" Perez and I spoke together.

"So you both know her? She was brought into Cas this morning, and I must get back to her when I've had a breather."

"Is she very ill?" I asked.

"Very. She's not even with us yet. I've drawn off a pint and a half of blood and got her on oxygen. Can you give me any clues, Perez?"

"Get her up to Sister Linden, old chap. That's your answer."

"Please, Doctor Smale, do—and put her next to me. There's a spare bed there."

"But she's very ill, June. You won't want her right next to you."

"Yes, please. I like her very much, so I don't care how unpleasant it is—and she'll drink pineapple juice before she'll touch anything else, and I've got some, and I can get Nurse to make up some of my jellies for her, and . . ."

Dr Smale cut me short. "Have you joined the staff here?"

"Joined the staff!" Perez raised his eyebrows. "I should think so. She's been treated as a member of the staff as long as I can remember. Visitors when she pleases. Lights on as long as she likes. Nurses scrambling eggs for her in the middle of the night. Orderlies tumbling over themselves to wheel her trolley——"

Dr Smale readjusted his feet on the balcony rail. "Do go on. I realized there were certain privileges accorded that corner bed, but tell me more—you got to the porters."

Perez had a look in his eye I did not like. "Well, then there was the time June did a locum for Dicky Nairn. A patient arrives in Alex. She's old, she's thin, and she's got spots on her tongue, inside her mouth, and on various parts of her body.

230

She says she lives alone—has to go out to work, and doesn't get time to buy decent food . . . so what does she do?"

"Starves."

"Only half. For the rest, she eats out of tins. Then she comes to us, sick and spotty. She's put next to June. Dicky Nairn takes a look at her on a Tuesday, makes his diagnosis, tells her she'll be cured but he wants to lecture on her on Thursday or Friday—then he goes away. The old lady is worried and tells June the doctor said she had scabies. June has seen plenty of scabies and she knows it's not that—she's heard about the tinned food—so decides Dicky Nairn must have said scurvy."

"Which is more likely."

"It was scurvy. But June doesn't stop there. She's learnt about vitamins at school. Scurvy means lack of vitamin C— plenty of vitamin C tablets on the medicine trolley and Nurse hands them out wholesale, so the answer is simple. June tells the old lady to ask for a handful. Couldn't do her any harm, and might cure her."

"Oh, no."

"A handful every time the trolley comes round. Result?"

Dr Smale was slapping his leg with one hand and holding his side with the other. "Don't tell me—no spots for Dicky Nairn's lecture?"

"Actually, Sister intervened in time. June was only trying to help. It couldn't do any harm—in fact, vitamin C was the answer."

"What did Dicky Nairn say?"

"He just looked."

"For the spots?"

"No—at our friend in the plaster bed."

Dr Smale shrugged himself into his coat. "June, I've under-estimated you." He went away laughing and shaking his head.

I was left on the balcony all day. I enjoyed having my visitors out there, because we could shed all formality and laugh and talk at will. As my trolley was being pushed up the ward in the evening I saw screens round the bed next to mine. Dr Smale's curly head appeared for a second over the top of one of them. He smiled and nodded so I knew Lydia Manning was there. She was shut off from me by screens and silence for five days before Sister came, in the middle of my morning's treatment, to tell me that I could speak to her.

"Please, Sister, tell her I can't see her until lunch time."

Sister looked across at Betty and they both smiled.

"I know—you will be sitting up."

Just before my own screens were moved from my bed at midday, I heard Lydia's being taken away. Then we were both smiling at each other across a small space, both sitting up. I leant forward, as far as I dared, and put my left arm over my shoulder, pretending to pat a pillow.

"Hallo, Lydia, I've been longing to see you."

Her eyes were popping. "My friend—but this is marvellous, yes? You sit up, you move your arm. I did not know. I did not think ever to see this. Already, I am made to feel better."

"Well, don't cry about it."

"We will have fun, yes? You and I."

"Yes, but you take it easy for a while." Her whole body jerked to the pounding of her heart. "How is your little boy?"

"He is the nice little man. He goes now to boarding school with other little mens, but he is, I think, the best. I am naughty mother, yes?"

Naughty, I thought, was right, not because of her pride in her son but because she had been driving herself, and an already overworked heart, to keep him in a school. I wondered how she would manage during the forthcoming weeks. She made beautiful animals. She cut her own patterns, put gay little hats and shoes on horses, windows in a snail's shell because she said children always want the snail's house to look like a house, hobnail boots on a mountain goat, dancing pumps on penguins, and pork pies on camels. There was no connection between a pork-pie hat and a camel, but it looked so ridiculous sitting on the head of the supercilious beast that the camels became a great attraction, and orders for them were heavy.

While Lydia stitched, Betty bent her silky brown head over my body and toiled. I swung aloft in my slings on the Balkan beam, which had now to withstand a weight that swung from

side to side and up and down. One day my legs, pulled sideways by some muscles at my waist, sent a screen hurtling to the
floor. Nurses coming in behind the screens with cups of tea,
mail, or messages, always peered over the top first to see where
they could enter without being knocked over. But if I har-
boured any misconceptions as to my physical prowess while I
was swinging, they were shattered as soon as I was lowered
onto my mattress, or into Jimmy, to become once more a heap
of flaccid flesh.

When I had been with Jimmy for a year and two weeks, Mr
Muir agreed to our separation. It was a very simple affair. One
day, instead of being put back in Jimmy for the night, I stayed
in my bed while he and his frame remained on the floor underneath it. The first night was one of peace, spaciousness, and
great joy; the second was torture. I wanted my plaster friend;
I missed his relaxing contours; I thought my back was going to
break; my hips felt as if they had been dislocated; and I had
cramp in my neck. I grizzled and moaned, then begged to be
put back. Night Nurse brought me a cup of tea and sat with
me. I still thought of Jimmy: but he remained under the bed.

Next day my aching body had settled down, and I was
ashamed of myself as I realized that Jimmy's departure took me
one step nearer a normal existence. Sister took him away from
my corner, to relieve the congestion, and put him temporarily
in the ward bathroom. There he leant disconsolately against a
cupboard until Staff Nurse had to go to the cupboard in an
emergency, and emergencies in hospital mean haste. She picked
Jimmy up and placed him face downwards in the bath. It was
dusk, and she had no sooner left the bathroom than an elderly
and feeble-sighted patient, from the small ward, stumbled
along to her evening wash. She did not bother to switch on the
light as she shuffled slowly towards the bath. We all heard her
scream. Sister and Staff Nurse rushed from one emergency to
what sounded like another. They found toilet perquisites scattered on the floor, and an old lady leaning against the wall
pointing wild-eyed at the bath. Sister explained that Jimmy
was only a lump of plaster, not a corpse, but his shape was
human enough to be mistaken for one. That really was the end

of him. A porter took him out the bottom door of the ward, and of his subsequent fate I heard nothing.

The morning after Jimmy's departure Betty Ainsworth came through the top door with a high-backed canvas wheel-chair, Miss Tudehope, and a tall, sandy-haired man in a white coat, who was introduced to me as a doctor of physical medicine. I thought I was acquainted with all the divisions and sub-divisions of the medical profession and their names, but this was something new. I was screened off, then pulled up my bed by the two physios, until my head was hanging free of the bed. The doctor of physical medicine stood behind the iron frame of the bed and held my head, as it was poked further into space. There were no down bars on the frame.

"Doctor is going to do a manipulation, June."

There was a voice behind me. "Just relax your head completely, will you?"

That was not difficult because I was not able to hold it for long in the position in which he held it. His hands were on either side of my face, and my head well back. There was a quick movement, I was looking at the floor, then the ceiling again. I began to doubt my eyes. Another quick movement, a pistol shot in my neck, I saw the floor, then the ceiling.

"Ah . . . that got it," said the voice behind me. "Will you let me do it again?"

"Yes, it's nice."

"Nice!" It was Betty.

"Yes, nice and free, as if something had been caught there for a long time."

The floor, the ceiling; the floor, the ceiling; and another sharp report like the crack of a whip. "That will do for today. I'll do it for a few days, then you can take over."

Betty looked up with her mouth agape. "Me, doctor?"

"Yes, this will have to go on for some time, I expect."

"Will it—will it always make that noise?"

"What—the cracks? Yes. That's what I want you to aim at. The more you can get, and the louder they are, the better. There's a lot there to be broken down. I'll be back tomorrow."

When he had gone I looked at Betty's stricken face. "Don't

worry, old thing—it feels grand, truly. What is it all in aid of anyway?"

"You know all that cramp you get?"

"Yes."

"Well, you've got a whole heap of adhesions in your neck and shoulder girdle—on the right side, where your paralysis is most severe."

"But you physios have never stopped moving my arms about—specially my shoulders."

"I know, but even that can't always prevent muscle fibres adhering. You have got what we call torticollis, and that's why your shoulders ache when you sit up, and why they're such a peculiar shape."

"Peculiar shape? What's peculiar about them?"

"Even lying down they are odd. You look at them." She held a mirror above me and pulled down the top of my gown.

"Great Scott! They go up instead of down, and my head's got a list to the right." The more I looked the more I laughed. "They look like a couple of canoes dipping in the middle and raised at both ends. Why are they like that?"

"Some of it caused by muscle wastage, but most of it from your respiratory trouble and your shallow breathing."

"But I breathe properly, now."

"Yes, but the deed was done before you started diaphragmatic breathing. Don't worry, we'll get it straightened out in time."

"I'm not worried . . . why did you bring a wheel-chair?"

"Good gracious! I forgot." She looked at Miss Tudehope. "Will you give me a quarter of an hour before lunch to put June into it?"

"Today?" I cried.

"Yes, today—but to work first, my girl."

Betty and Miss Tudehope rolled me into a dressing-gown, put operation socks on my legs, draped a rug over the chair, and began their struggle. I laughed with excitement but it was no fun for them. Nurse came to assist and, by lunch-time, I was pulled up alongside Lydia.

"This gets every day better, my friend. Now we eat both at the same table." She laughed, and made a flat place on her counterpane. "My bed it is table, yes? You are happy. All the time your eyes they smile. Now you think, perhaps you go about, yes?"

"Perhaps, Lydia, but I haven't got my spinal brace, and I don't think I'll be allowed to stay in this very long in case I start to sag."

"It is in the back?"

"Yes—but you, Lydia, you look miles better. Are the doctors pleased?"

She laughed and threw out her hands. "The doctors make long faces at my bed. They put little blue spot on my side with the ink, they put cold thing on little blue spot, then all around is quiet while they listen through their earholes. They make long faces at little blue spot, and they talk. Then they again listen, and again talk. Then all the young ones with no coats, called students, they listen, and they make long faces. Then I hear one doctor say that it is noise like train in tunnel, and I laugh because that is my heart he calls train. I would like very much to listen too—but I feel, and perhaps that is enough."

She leant forward and laid her hand on my arm. "My friend, I look many times at you, and I think much, but I do not know now the answer. What is the worst, I think, to have good muscles but the heart so bad that I cannot go about?—or to have good heart but the muscles so bad that you cannot go about. What you think?"

"I think you're a very nice person, Lydia."

Sister came up the ward with a wide smile.

"You two haven't stopped talking for the last half-hour. Now, you have a rest, Mrs Manning, while I take June around the ward."

"A round tour, Sister?"

"Yes. Would you like it?"

"Oh, yes, please. I'll make a report as I go."

"A report?"

"Yes, you know—pillows turned round the wrong way and showing the ticking, corners that aren't enveloped, casters

236

sticking out at angles, patients not lying in a straight line in the centre of their beds, lockers——"

"June, stop it, or I shan't take you." But she was laughing.

As we pulled away from Lydia's bed, and began to go down the ward, my lips parted, and I started to sing the Marseillaise. The chair stopped.

"What shall I do with her, Doctor Smale?"

"I'm afraid she's a hopeless case, Sister. Better carry on marching."

She marched me into the kitchen, then through the stone archway into the small ward. A tiny face, and a sheen of white hair, lay on a pillow under FRANCES JAYCOX I.

"Would you like to go and see Perez for a few minutes, June?"

"Please."

She clipped the door back, and wheeled me in: past the first bed, and alongside the second. Perez dropped a book he was reading onto his lap. "Sister! Have you brought June to see me?"

"For a few minutes only. She must go back to bed soon."

"I am honoured . . . but, Sister, I warn you, now she has started wandering, your troubles have begun."

"I know. She began today by singing as soon as she felt the chair moving—the Marseillaise of all things."

The face in the bed was alight. "I know exactly how you feel, Sister. Leave her here, and I'll give her some singing lessons."

"Ten minutes, June—then, to bed."

"Yes, Sister, and thank you."

As soon as Betty arrived to give me my afternoon's treatment, I told her I had been visiting.

"I am not surprised. I guessed something like that would happen. I even prepared myself for a barrage of questions by asking Mr Muir how soon it would be before you could start going out."

"OUT?"

"I mean outside St Mary's. There's a limit to how far a wheelchair can be pushed, but you'll be able to see something of London."

"When?"

"When you can sit in your chair for two hours without

sagging. And now, will you stop looking so pop-eyed, and do some work.''

Next morning Staff Nurse came in behind the screens to watch my head being manipulated. After the first crack she fled. I tried to make Betty understand that it was most enjoyable, and that I felt no pain at all. She was accustoming herself to the thought of doing it but she did not relish it.

"It's all right for you, June. You can't see what the doctor does. He screws your head round so fast, and so far, that I feel sure your neck will break, and on top of that there's those frightful noises that sound like bones being snapped in half. It's ghastly.''

Despite her fears Betty turned out to be an excellent manipulator and prided herself on the number of cracks she could produce in one manipulation. Quite often she had an audience.

A tall cupboard was carried into the ward and put in the corner between my bed and the wall. It was for my clothes: a pair of warm slacks, blouses, jumpers, and cardigans, brought from my trunks. The first day they arrived I never took my eyes off them, and when someone closed the door on them, I gazed at the wooden cupboard and could still see my clothes hanging inside it.

My back grew stronger and, one Sunday, I sat up for two hours in my wheel-chair. I was put to bed, where I indulged in a little idle day-dreaming. I was sorry Lydia was not next to me. Towards evening Dr Smale walked up the ward and sat down on a chair alongside my bed.

"Congratulations. Now—about going out. Will you let me take you for your first trip? I thought of going to Hyde Park.''

I swallowed. "I'd love it, you know that, but you're much too busy.''

"I have Wednesday afternoon off.''

"But you can't give up your free afternoon just for me.''

"I'll enjoy it as much as you. It's settled, then.''

"But what about treatment?''

He groaned aloud. "You ought to have a club tied to your bed, so that we can hit you with it when you make remarks like that. Do you think for one moment that the physiotherapists, or Mr Muir, or Duggy Timms, or Sister Linden, or anyone else, would prevent you from getting out of hospital for a couple of hours the first time it had become possible?"

At midday on Wednesday it started to drizzle with rain. Betty flattened her face against the window. "I could think of a number of things to call the weather—none of them polite or pleasant. But we'll get you dressed."

"Oh well, I shall gaze at the plane tree, and pretend I'm in Hyde Park."

Betty looked up. She held a slipper in her hand. "See this?"

"Yes, size seven, goes on the left foot."

"It will go somewhere else if you're not very careful."

Fully dressed, I lay on my bed and fed myself without seeing what I was doing: my eyes were on the window. At five minutes to two Dr Smale walked in and my heart leapt. He was wearing a heavy tweed coat and carrying a light grey mackintosh. We were going out.

He bent over the bed. "Hang on with what you've got, June." His face was red as he bundled me into the chair. He straightened up. "How much do you weigh? I've never lifted anybody as heavy as you, and I'm sure I've lifted fatter ones."

"Dead weight."

"I suppose so. All set, nurse? Quite warm, June?"

A rug was wrapped round my legs, and the raincoat pulled over my shoulders. "Yes, thank you."

"Good-bye, Sister."

"Good-bye, June. Take care of her, Doctor Smale."

"I'll tip her out if she gets cheeky, but I'll pick her up and bring her back again, never fear."

The chair moved quickly. "Her Bitt! Alex."

"Doctor Smale?"

"Yes, June."

"Please—if we meet anyone in the hall, or in Casualty, who wants to talk——"

"You leave it to me. We've got a train to catch until we get outside."

Ropes going down, a black shape coming up, and a clang of iron doors.

"Hallo, Herbert."

"'Ullo, miss."

We were soon clear of the hospital. "If you want to stop and look at anything just give the word, otherwise I'll make straight for the park."

Hyde Park on a wet Wednesday afternoon is something I shall never forget. There are but a few days in every year that we can recall with detailed clarity because they are exceptional, but that day stands out in my life. A cloud of misty rain shrouded trees that seemed to huddle together for shelter; a silver-grey twist of water that was the Serpentine; grass that was soft, and clean, and trailing raindrops; a dog that swallowed a stone; a walking stick; a well-cut coat; and an immense reach of grey sky.

Dr Smale rested an elbow on the stonework of a bridge crossing the Serpentine, keeping his other hand on the back of the chair. We were both gazing up the wind-whipped water into a landscape of subtly blended greys and greens.

"What's the matter with the young lady? Can't she walk?"

I turned with gaping mouth, to see a woman standing close to the front of the chair looking down at the rug, which covered my legs. My mouth banged shut as the chair shot forward with violence, and lurched twice.

A wail of anguish. "Ow! You've run over my feet."

A quiet voice behind me. "Yes, and I'm really sorry I haven't done any damage."

We bowled along the footpath.

"She won't be the only one either. I'll have to get used to being stared at and questioned."

"Yes, I'm afraid you will. But to have that on your first day out . . ."

"Next time it happens tell whoever it is that you ran over me with your car, and that this is all part of the compensation I am claiming."

"Can't I knock them about a bit as well?"

"Yes, of course—afterwards."

We went off the bridge with laughter and rain in our faces.

Chapter 21

A COW IN THE GYMNASIUM

———∿∿∿⅃⎛⦿⎞⌐∿∿∿———

Six months after the plaster moulds of my body had been taken the instrument maker called for a first sitting. Although I had accustomed myself to the sight of callipers while I was in the country, I was not prepared for the weird and vast amount of ironmongery that was carried in. It was rough, unpolished, and ugly. There was a cumbersome leather spinal jacket, with steel supports up either side, and a steel brace round my pelvis and abdomen. The leg callipers looked singularly long and unwieldy. Two strong steel shafts, running down either side of my legs, fitted into the heels of my shoes. The knees were hinged, and had bolts that could be slipped up or down, thus locking and unlocking the callipers. The shafts were straightened and locked to keep my knees from buckling under me, when I was standing: the bolts were drawn up and the calliper bent, when I was seated. There was a further pair of adjustable bolts at the hips, where two butterfly screws pinned the outside shafts of the callipers to the steel side-supports of the jacket.

I lay on my bed while five people wrestled with steel and leather, my body, and a pair of pale blue silk pyjamas. Mr Kyte used a monkey wrench, a screwdriver, two spanners, a ruler, a pair of cutting shears, and a hammer.

"You haven't got a brace and bit in that bag, have you?"

He looked up from toil that was streaking his face with sweat. "I have, actually—but I hope I don't have to use it."

I gathered instruments were rather like railway lines: they had to meet and fit with fractional exactitude. It was difficult to say where the fault lay. I was swivelled about, tossed from one side to the other, pulled into a sitting position and laid down again, and still the hip bolts would not slip. They took it all off and started again: then, after a very long time, they managed to make both ends meet squarely and the bolts shot home.

I was secured.

Mr Kyte eased his aching back and looked at Betty. "We can't possibly get her on her feet today—not after this." He mopped his face and turned to me. "Sorry, lass, but you couldn't stand it."

So they unlocked me, and I lay on the bed in my pale blue pyjamas and slept.

The following evening I was collected by Perez and Dr Smale, and taken to a concert in the medical school. No plaster beds and trolleys now: but a light, high-backed, canvas wheel-chair that was easy to manipulate. Down in the lift to the basement, along a corridor, and into the tunnel that ran under the street. The tunnel was very dimly lit, and Dr Smale was not a slow man, even behind a push chair.

They drew the chair up alongside a row of seats in the library of the medical school, and sat down next to me. A man jumped up from the row opposite, and in a few strides was in front of me, leaning both hands on the arms of my chair and peering into my face. I glanced quickly at Perez and Dr Smale, but they looked as blank as I felt.

"Aren't you the girl from New Zealand, who contracted polio in Cairo on the way over here?"

"Yes, at least, they seem to think that's where I picked it up."

"But, damme . . . you're supposed to be dead!"

"I beg your pardon?"

He stood up. "I say, I'm awfully sorry. But I can't believe my eyes, I saw you when you were first ill—I was just off to South Africa, and believe me . . ." He walked round to view my back, then came and stood in front of me again. "I'm jolly glad I saw you. Thanks a lot." And he had gone.

I turned to my companions. "Did I come to listen to a piano recital, or a strange doctor who questions my right to be alive?"

Dr Smale leant across Perez. "You came to a recital—you are

staying to a recital, but—you are not going straight back to the ward after the recital.''

"Why ever not?''

"Because I am leaving St Mary's, and I'm having a farewell party, and you are coming.''

"Night Sister?''

"Night Sister we shall circumvent, if it is necessary, but I don't think it will be.''

"Thanks very much. What are you chuckling about, Perez?''

"Well, you know, I was just thinking that you could farewell Tony in gallons of pure alcohol if you wished. You don't have to walk home.''

Dr Smale had taken me on as many trips as he could. He was no respecter of persons and if he thought anyone was staring too pointedly, or approaching us with a question on his lips, he used the force of his tongue, and the chair, in quashing them. I was prepared for any eventuality.

The weather grew cold, and I could not have gone out, even if Dr Smale had still been on Alex. The nurses gave my hair its first proper wash by hanging my head over the edge of the bed and washing my hair in a bucket of soapy water on a stool below. It was not only the first time my hair had been washed since I was ill; it was also the first time my hair had been washed without my eyes being filled with soap.

Sister appeared inside the screens while the operation was being performed. One nurse supported my head while the other one soaped vigorously. I lay in comfort, smiling benignly.

"Tomorrow, June,'' Sister said, "you will have a bath.''

"But I have a bath every morning.''

"I don't mean a blanket bath, I mean a proper one.''

Two physios and a nurse blocked their ears against the noise of my singing the next day.

"Oh, June—do you have to? It's time you came out, any-way.''

But I was slippery, and when they did manage to get a grip on me, they could not hold it, and lift as well. They dare not let the water out because they needed a certain amount to float me within grabbing range. A crane would have been necessary to lift me from an empty bath. I wallowed and sang, while they pondered.

They made one more attempt but it failed, largely, I think, because we laughed too much. Eventually, they went for help. Two physios and four nurses, with rumpled wet uniforms; one polio washed, dried, dusted with powder, happy, and unmindful.

Sister Linden met the chair halfway up the ward. "Nice bath, June?"

"Glorious, Sister—and really, it was no trouble."

"She can have one every week, nurse."

Nurse gulped. "Yes, Sister."

One day, while I was sitting in my chair, I fulfilled a desire which had grown more intense with every day of my illness. With my stronger left arm I pulled my right over and round the arm of the chair, and, with the fingers of my right hand, I caught hold of the belt of my dressing-gown. I was looped and anchored to the chair. I hoped I should remain so.

I leant forward cautiously and let my left arm drop down in front of my knees, before worming it inside the rug. For the first time in five hundred and seventy-three days I could scratch my legs. Once started, I went crazy.

"June!" It was a horrified gasp from a nurse. My left hand was seized round the wrist and held.

"Please, nurse—please. Let me go. Please—they're my legs." I was frantic, and kept my head bent trying to pull my hand towards my legs again. But I was no match for nurse. I'll bite her, I thought—and I meant it. "Please, nurse, please."

"What is the matter?" It was the quiet voice of the new houseman.

"Oh, Doctor St Clair, June's scratching her legs. Look at them. Ugh!"

"It's the very first time I've ever been able to do it. Please, nurse, let me go."

"Nurse—release her hand."

"But she'll make her legs bleed. Look, she's drawn blood in one place already."

"Release her hand, nurse."

My nails were tearing into my legs again with a wild, reckless abandon that was ecstasy.

"You do not consider it very hygienic, or dignified, nurse? I suggest you help June rather than hinder her."

"Help her! Not to scratch? Oh, doctor, no."

There was a chuckle of laughter. "No, not to scratch. But quite soon this scratching woman will have done enough blood letting to satisfy herself. Bring a bowl of warm water and wash her legs, then dab them with mercurocrome wherever the skin is broken."

"Yes, doctor."

I had a wonderful time.

The days had wings. The year was passing, Christmas was coming again, and we had given up all hope of seeing my instruments until the New Year. But one grey December day Mr Kyte pushed open the top door of the ward, with a bundle of winking steel and polished leather in his arms, received a smile and an affirmative nod from Sister, and came quickly over to my bed.

His bundle made an arresting sight, far too arresting: there seemed to be too much of it, but both legs, the spinal brace, a bundle of laces, and some shiny screws, had luggage labels with my name printed in large letters attached to them, so there could not have been any mistake. I did wonder if there would be enough of me to fit in all of it. After thirty-five minutes I changed my ideas and wondered if, perhaps, there was too much of me to fit the harness.

My head and arms were the only parts of me not encased in something solid and immovable, and my flopping right arm persistently got in the way. Mr Kyte picked it up and looked at Betty.

"Is this hand strong enough to hold a crutch?"

"Yes, quite. We'll have to watch her arm carefully, though."

They stood and considered. How were they going to get me to my feet? I wondered what it would feel like to stand up in shoes again. I was lying flat on the bed and I was as unbending as six feet of railway line because I had to be locked into a straight line before they heaved me to my feet. I was much thicker than six feet of railway line, and much heavier. They swivelled me round so that I lay across the bed, but a bed is not very wide: two feet of me lay across the bed while nearly four feet of me shot horizontally into space. The two physios pressed my legs downwards, Mr Kyte shoved from behind, and as I began to change from a horizontal railway line to a vertical one he clambered across the bed, still pushing from behind. The physios jammed their feet against my toes as they struck the floor and changed their tactics from pushing to pulling.

I was erect.

I had only time to notice that I was taller than anyone present and that there was a dirty black roof-top directly below my window when I felt myself sliding—not hurriedly—to the floor. I could come to no possible harm—the steel and leather took all the bumps—but now I was a heavy horizontal unbending mass that had to be raised from floor level.

After three Herculean attempts Mr Kyte sat on the bed and mopped his brow. They unlocked me, made me bend, heaved me back onto the bed, locked me, levered me to my feet again, and hung onto me. A pair of solid wooden crutches were pushed under my armpits, I grasped the handles and hung onto them: but Betty and Miss Tudehope were taking no chances and while I hung onto the crutches they hung onto me. All I did that day was stand, in one spot, getting what Betty called the "feel of things".

That night I glanced up from the book I was reading towards the door of the cupboard in my corner. My callipers were leaning against it. I would become accustomed to them in time, but not too accustomed I hoped, because I wanted always to think of them as a means to an end: not an end in themselves. I made up my mind, then and there, that they would go the way of the iron lung, the Paul Brag, Jimmy, and his better half.

The following day I stood on my own: that is, without any support from the physios, but I have grave doubts as to whether an observer, who had no previous knowledge of the case, would have described five feet nine and a half inches of callipered and braced body, draped over two underarm crutches, as standing on its own. I did.

"Feeling all right, June?"

I looked down into the top of Sister's white starched bonnet as she stood beside me: then a pair of brown eyes were raised to mine.

"Do you think you've grown, June?"

"No, Sister, quite sure. I've been as tall as this since I was sixteen. When I think of last Christmas and Jimmy, and now, this——" I looked down at my harness. "In its own way it really is quite a sizable and wonderful Christmas present. I begin to appreciate it."

Sister had been walking round me chewing the stem of her spectacles, but, as I stopped speaking, she came to a halt in front of me, and gave a rueful grin. "I'm afraid you won't appreciate what has just come into the ward."

"The new patient? Oh, Sister," I groaned, "not another Mrs Feeny-Barb?"

"No, but you are close."

"Thyroid toxicosis?"

"Yes, and she's several degrees more excitable than the one last year."

Her name was Sadie, she was Swiss-German, and broken English poured from her mouth in an unceasing, almost unintelligible, stream. She was loud and coarse. She talked while I walked, and my method of getting myself over the floor was as far removed from any semblance of walking as was her thick guttural noisiness from what one normally regards as talking.

My corner of the ward became Sister's nightmare. Instead of the six square feet allotted to each patient my things filled nine cubic feet. Books, flowers, food parcels from home, a case of fruit under the bed, spare pillows and blankets, a locker popeyed with "necessaries", the clothes cupboard, plaster splints for night wear, some large oil-paintings, callipers and back brace that would never stand in a neat pile, two long wooden crutches, and the wheel-chair—all this had, in theory, to be immaculately and compactly stowed around me. Anything within a three-foot radius of my bed was given a wide berth and I lay in a growing mountain of decorations, undisturbed by ward routine as Christmas approached.

The New Year saw me in the gymnasium, a long wooden building abutting on the Paddington horse stables. It was a long journey by wheel-chair. We turned off Praed Street to bump along a cobble-stoned terrace that was land-marked by an old gas street lamp, seemingly growing from the middle of it. I always gambled privately on which side of the lamp my charioteers would pass. Two strides down a little blind street running at right angles to the cobbled terrace and we were in front of the main doors of the gymnasium.

The gymnasium was like a drill hall when it was empty, but when it was full of struggling bodies at various stages of returning mobility, and physiotherapists instructing individuals or conducting classes, it was what I imagined the inside of a huge circus marquee would look like if all the performers were practising their separate acts at once. There were broken necks, broken legs, broken toes, osteo-arthritis, fibrositis, strains, sprains, polios, spastics, and all manner of crippling diseases with long technical names. Classes were conducted where possible: usually with fracture and ante-natal patients. Otherwise a patient had to be treated individually and in such cases a physiotherapist was specifically allocated.

No one took the slightest notice of how well I could walk, or whether I could walk at all. Crutches, sticks, plasters, artificial limbs, callipers and wheel-chairs were littered about. I felt at home. There was no pity: only laughter and encouragement. My embarrassment was quickly overcome by the necessity of concentrating on what I was doing. There was no time to stand and stare at myself or anyone else.

With a sturdy wooden crutch jabbed under each armpit, and my harness securely bolted about me, I began to walk again. I shook; I perspired; sometimes I swore under my breath; often I fell over; always I had to think very hard. I had to learn to balance on my two feet and the crutch under my right arm in order to pick up the crutch under my left arm and move it forward a few inches over the floor: then I shifted the weight of my cumbersome body onto the two crutches and my right foot while I scuffled my left foot forward a few inches over the floor: one step. Hot, tiring, work; a smiling, patient Betty Ainsworth: a stubborn and sometimes angry New Zealand polio. I mumbled to myself: "Move left crutch, move left foot, move right crutch—watch wobbly arm—now, right foot, I must try and keep my head up, move left crutch, move left foot, I'm not really tired, move right crutch—damn!" Out loud I said:

"Betty! I'm falling."

"Crutches, June."

As I spun through space I pushed as hard as I could with my arms to throw my crutches clear. That is one lesson that has to be learnt very early because there is no easier way to break an arm than to fall with it grasping a crutch; and arms are important to polios who have paralysis of both legs.

Providing I had suffered no injury I was put on my feet immediately after a fall so that I could carry on. There was plenty of space in the gym. I was grateful because I was tall and required quite a lot of room in which to fall unimpeded.

Stretched out on the floor one day, fitting punishment for imagining that I could take longer strides than Betty thought advisable, I heard a deep voice, and steps, coming up the gymnasium towards us.

"Quick! Put me on my feet again please. Here comes Mr Muir."

"You'll stay there awhile, my girl. You bumped your head a bit harder than usual that time."

Two pairs of feet alongside me. I looked up. I came to the top of the head of the physio department and I continued looking up. A tie, revers of a pin-stripe suit, a white collar, and still I looked up.

"Hurt, June?"

"No, Mr Muir, but Miss Ainsworth insists on me having a rest."

"Why did you fall?"

"Disobeying instructions about taking smaller steps."

They talked for a while before putting me on my feet. I was nervous, not from my fall but because I was conscious of a pair of eyes watching me: eyes that saw movement which a brain translated almost simultaneously into a detailed anatomical chart of exactly what was happening inside the steel and leather harness. I ploughed on down the gymnasium: one crutch, one foot, one crutch, one foot. I spoke softly to myself. "Go slowly —it is better to go slowly than fall over in front of him." I was a long time turning round because there was a great deal of crutch and foot manipulation involved in the manœuvre. But I got there and started to plod back: one crutch, one foot, one crutch, one foot. Betty had a steadying arm and my chair ready. She unbolted me and I dropped into the canvas seat, wet with sweat and shaky.

Mr Muir came round from behind the chair. "That was a great effort—good girl." I felt a firm hand on my shoulder and was amazed because it had not been put there to test my muscles.

In the afternoon of the same day he arrived in Alex with a group of students.

"Tired?"

"A little, Mr Muir."

"You have a rest while I talk." He turned to the students. "I want to introduce you to my Antipodean quadruped."

The sudden explosion of my laughter caught everyone unawares. The big man hid a smile for a while but my unrestrained mirth, and the bewilderment of the students, brought a gleam to his eyes and his mouth began to broaden.

"You've hit the nail right on the head, Mr Muir. I walk exactly like a cow. I've been trying to think what I resemble— but that's it. One crutch, one foot, one crutch, one foot, four legs instead of two, head dropping forward." I looked at the students grouped about my bed. "That is just what I'm like— a cow. Ever seen a cow in a gymnasium?"

It was a rather hilarious lecture, as the big man kept making frequent references to quadraplegics and quadrupeds and the students were catching the humour of the situation even while they were absorbing orthopaedic knowledge.

Chapter 22

FORE AND AFT

At the beginning of my third year as a polio I began to
grow up again. I began to wash myself, to comb my
hair and plait it; I could clean my teeth, cut my finger-
nails, cut my food and put it in my mouth; help Betty by lower-
ing slings, holding electrical discs, and often operating the battery. I could not roll over in bed or lift my heavy limbs about
by myself, but I could see that the day would come when I
should be able to do so. All these things were not done with
the speed and dexterity that one usually expects from an adult;
but I did them, and as I laboured slowly, with weak unsynchronized muscles that shook at the thought of physical exertion and often let me down, I recognized the one great virtue
of poliomyelitis.

It is a disease that is numbered among the nastiest in the
medical world because of its consequences, but it is the one
major crippling disease I know of that is not degenerative. It
is a disease which strikes suddenly, and from which the recovery is slow, but once the initial attack is over there is no
question of the sufferer's becoming worse. Always we improve,
and the chances are that we shall regain a hundred per cent
mobility. That does not necessarily mean a hundred per cent
return to normal muscle power. Any polio severely paralysed
at the onset realizes that a few things must go, but the fact that
there are patches of weak muscles and sometimes patches where
there are no muscles at all does not mean that one is immobilized for the rest of one's life. Recovery is protracted, sometimes boring, and always tiring because of the mental concen-
tration required.

In the gym impatience and anger fought with stubbornness

and laughter, but always I felt well and knew that I was improving. Those are the blessings of the polio: never to feel ill, never to go down hill, and never to have pain except at the very beginning. I never knew what I was going to do next, but I made up my mind that I should walk again and that I should accept, with a fair measure of equanimity, most of the things that happened between immobility and mobility. It was taking years, but it was worth it. I laughed too much and was often too weak with giggles to respond sensibly to instructions. I could not get the picture of myself as a cow out of my mind. Apart from all this I was making lifelong friends among the young nurses, students, physios, and doctors in St Mary's. I had polio to thank for that.

It brought only one thing I hated. It was something that dogged my footsteps wherever I went, it followed my chair, it sometimes—but not often—hung over my bed, and it was something I refused to accept because it carried a destructive force of which I was frightened. I determined to kill it quickly wherever I found it no matter how painful its death was to its propagator. It was pity. Not pity that brings help, and advice, and a sympathetic understanding—that is necessary, and of inestimable value: but the "Oh, you poor girl! Why should this happen to you?" approach.

There was not a soul on the staff of St Mary's who was ever once guilty of it. Outside, I developed an attitude of jocular, but rather forthright, rudeness towards it.

Every added accomplishment brought a little well of happiness that I shall never forget: it was a happiness that grew inside me. I always sat up in my chair for lunch and sitting thus, by the bedside of a new patient one day, I was waiting for my plateful of dinner when I heard a whisper from the bed.

"My dear, could you cut my meat for me, please?"

I looked at her hands. They were knotted and twisted with rheumatoid arthritis and the flesh wasted between each swollen joint. "Of course," I said, and reached out my arm to take her plate.

As I sat with it on my knee, cutting the meat into cubes that I had found so easy to manipulate, I could not laugh. For some reason this was bigger than laughter. I was sitting there cutting someone else's meat for them. Something caught in my throat and my eyes filled with tears. I handed the plate back.

"Thank you very much."

"June! you're not crying?"

"Sorry, Doctor Hume, but I ran out of laughter. I've been cutting up this patient's meat, that's all."

He smiled his wide handsome smile. "You have my permission to give your halo a twist."

I laughed then and got on with my own dinner.

But I was not content with this. One day I decided to take the matter of my recovery out of Mr Muir's and Dr Timms's hands into my own trembling ones. I was sitting on the edge of my bed, legs a-dangle, an operation gown tied with one string behind my neck, and a dressing-gown draped loosely over my shoulders. The canvas chair was pushed inside the screens surrounding my bed and I was hanging onto the top of my locker while Nurse rummaged through the bottom of it, searching for some operation socks to put on my blue legs. She looked up.

"Will you be safe, June, while I dash away and get a pair of socks? I can't find any in here."

"Yes, nurse, quite safe."

"Won't be a moment."

She went quickly out of the screens.

I must not waste any time. I edged the locker a little nearer the bed with my strong left arm, got a firm grip on it with my skinny right fingers, pushed the dressing-gown off my shoulders: then I looked at my blue legs almost dangling on the floor. I must hurry because Nurse would soon be back. My stomach, slack with weak muscles, began to quiver, but it was no use getting the shakes if I was going to do what I wanted to do. I took one last look at everything, tried to get a picture of myself in relation to the objects enclosed by the screens, and decided that the locker was my safest bet. I sidled further towards the edge of the bed until my feet touched the floor and my body was well over the locker: then I stood up.

There was a sickening crash.

"Nurse! Oh, nurse! June's fallen."

Lying with my bare back on the cold floor, one leg under the bed, the other squashed against my locker, and my head on the foot-rest of the chair that had collected a screen as the force of my fall pushed it back, I thought what an unnecessary remark the patient next to me had made. I also thought what a fool I had been. But, with the luck of all fools, I had done no more than injure my knee.

They bundled me back into bed, put my leg to rest in a plaster splint, and raised it on some pillows. No one thought it was very funny, nor did they commend me for my spirit of adventure. Sometime later Mr Muir and Mr Pastaad-Noyes came in and threw back the bedclothes and cradle covering my leg.

"Mr Muir—this is all my own fault, you know. Nurse left me quite safely on the bed, but I——"

"Decided you would try and stand by yourself—no callipers, no crutches?" He was bending over my leg. It was shiny and swollen and the flesh was hard to his touch.

"Yes."

"Frightened?"

"Of what you are going to say? A little."

He turned to face me then, and for the first, and only, time in the many hours I had watched this big man, I caught him off guard. There was compassion in his eyes: but only for a second. "I'd have done the same thing myself." He looked down at his own body. "And I should probably have made more of a mess of things than you did." He was smiling: so was I. "When I asked you if you were frightened I was referring to the fall. Did that frighten you?"

"Yes."

"Would you be frightened of falling again?"

"No."

"Good, because you will have many falls as you learn to walk again. But let your callipers cover the breakages until you are stronger and learn to fall properly. Exercise what control you have over your movements while you are dropping through space and then you will reduce your injuries to a minimum."

"You mean, like turning somersaults in the air when you're diving from a high board?"

"Exactly. But I don't expect you to turn somersaults before you hit the floor. We don't want this," pointing to my leg, "to happen again. It's going to put you back."

It did put me back, because I could not walk on it, but Betty turned the situation to good account by launching a concentrated attack on my back. I began to sit up all day without sagging or flagging and without my spinal brace. I was taken out more than I deserved by my ever-faithful English visitors.

I visited art galleries, museums, theatres, and cinemas; Peter took me to the Albert Hall; Stephen's aunt and uncle took me to Covent Garden, to opera and ballet. I was seeing London, and I loved every moment of it. I visited English homes, went for long drives in London and out of London. It seemed that everyone had some special place they were determined that I should see, once I could be taken about in cars. I had picnics in Richmond Park, Epping Forest, and on the top of the Hog's Back. I saw everything with eyes that were greedy to grasp and retain all England's beauty. They could not do it, but they carry always a picture of two swans cutting through a thin crust of ice on a lake, like ships in an ice floe; an almond tree in bloom against the grey stone of an English church; the clean trunk of a plane tree stripped of winter blackness; the curving greenness of the countryside; the keeper's lodge in Kensington Gardens: a host of things and, with them, the faces and voices of the people who made it all possible.

A Friday evening, and Peter striding across the ward to greet me. He bent close.

"You look all lit up. What's to do?"

"You see that thing over there in the corner?" I was pointing at my spinal brace which was standing between the cupboard and the wall.

"Yes."

"Well, today Mr Muir told me that I don't need a full brace any longer, so it's going to be cut in half, clean in half. It's going to be reduced to an abdominal brace. It's only a beginning, but——"

"A beginning of the gradual break-up of the rest of your harness?"

"Yes. At least, that's how I feel about it."

"You have quite a collection on the compost heap already, haven't you? The lung, the respirator, your plaster beds, drinking tubes, your bookstand, your backrest, and probably innumerable things I know nothing about. Altogether, they've ironed out quite a few kinks in you, haven't they?"

The ironing went on until one glorious June day Sister Linden, Dr Timms, and Mr Muir, came together to my bedside. They were all smiling. Dr Timms was closest to me.

"Well, June," he said, "how would you like to go home?"

I looked from one smiling face to the other and still could not believe. "To New Zealand, Doctor Timms?"

"Yes."

"You really mean that?"

"Yes."

"When can I go? And how?" The questions poured out.

They answered them all and, finally, I was convinced that it was true.

Mr Muir looked down. "You need sunshine, June, and good food, and sleep. You must catch up on all of them. Coming at this stage, a sea voyage is the best thing for you."

The High Commissioner, Peter, and my friends did all the work connected with my journey home, while Betty worked harder than ever on my body, determined that I should enjoy the trip to the full. I began to take my first shuffling steps without any instruments at all, although I had to lean on two people because I could not manage with my crutches. I walked without my callipers in the gym between two hand rails which were screwed to the floor. I purchased a pair of elbow crutches that were to act as intermediaries between underarm crutches and walking-sticks. My purchase was queried because no one could see how I was going to manage without underarm crutches, but I was taking them home; and I was determined to use them.

I wondered how I could thank all these people. They had

given me back my life, and there was nothing I could give them in return . . . but the House Governor decided, apparently, that they had not done enough. Sister came to my bed one day, her eyes alight with surprise.

"What do you think, June—I met the House Governor in the hall just now, and he said that he wants you to have a farewell party at St Mary's! In the Board Room."

"But—isn't the Board Room the holy of holies?"

Sister just smiled.

The House Governor did not believe in half measures; he had invitations printed and sent out; the hospital chef and kitchen staff were busy with lobsters and hors d'œuvre; the catering officer was put in charge of liquid refreshments; and two Sisters were made responsible for the flowers. It was to be a cocktail party and I thought I knew all about it. In an evening frock for the first time in two and a half years I arrived in the Board Room and saw the cake. It was a masterpiece. Green lace trailed over a white foundation. On the top was an enormous rose sepal in shades of green and rimmed with gold. It was tilted back a little, and from its inside spilled thirty-six tiny, but perfect, roses in shades of red, pink, and cream. Round the outside edge were five white shields, also rimmed with gold; one bore the initials S.M.H., another the fleur-de-lis emblem of St Mary's; one bore my initials, another the silver fern emblem of New Zealand; the last had "Bon Voyage" printed on it. All this in icing. It stood on a small table in the centre of the room with a silver vase of red roses on either side of it.

"Sister, do you think—would it be possible, to get a photograph of it before we eat it?"

"I'll get Linklater from the path lab." It was Perez who spoke.

"What about Doctor Meiklejohn, Perez? He's coming."

"Good idea. I'll ask him when he comes."

There were a great number of people in the Board Room and my thoughts were chaotic as I looked about me, knowing full well what each person meant in terms of my happiness. The Mary's people jostled with my visitors, and the High Commissioner, Dr Timms, Mr Muir, the House Governor, Dr

Nairn, and the New Zealand surgeon who had lent me the prismatic glasses formed a group in one corner of the room. There was plenty to eat, and plenty to drink; there were speeches and toasts; and late, far too late, the doctor called Linklater started taking photographs of the cake as I was about to cut it. Mr Muir, Dr Timms, Sister, and the High Commissioner stood behind the table, I sat to one side with a knife poised above the sepal and the roses. Cocktail parties are usually hourly affairs. This was not. I lost count of the hours, but I did spend part of the night back in Alex in my bed.

Next day one photograph was brought up from the path lab. All the others were reported to be fuzzy or out of focus. In the one that remained Dr Timms had lost an arm, Sister Linden's head was tilted so far back that all we could see was her chin and a wide smile, the High Commissioner's face was bent forwards and completely lost in shadows, I looked both pop- and cross-eyed. Mr Muir and the cake were not in the picture at all.

We roared.

"Do I really look like that?"

Perez grinned. "Not often, June—fortunately."

It was not very pleasant saying good-bye. Lydia was the only one who wept, but her illness forced her to live a secluded life which brought her few friends on whom she could lavish the affection that was so much a part of her nature. She had never visited me because the journey was too much for her pounding heart, but two nights before I left she came slowly in at the top door of the ward. I was pleased, and angry. We talked for a long time before she got up to go: then she took my hand in hers, while tears rolled unheeded down her cheeks.

"My friend," she said, "I come again to St Mary's when the heart it is very bad. But the next time when I come I do not go away, because the next time is the last time. So, my most dear friend, it has been pleasure, but this is my really good-bye to you—that is why I make strength for myself to come tonight. There is not much strength left, so I must say good-bye forever."

Dr Timms came, by himself, to my bedside; not as the

258

neurologist who had diagnosed and cared for me, nor as Dean of the Medical School; but as a trusted and well-established friend, with whom I had shared my personal problems, and for whom I felt much affection and esteem. We talked for some time.

"We are not letting you go because the battle is over, June. You realize that, don't you?"

"Yes, Doctor Timms, fully. And the responsibility of the battle will come to rest more and more with me as my mobility increases, won't it?"

"Yes. You will need direction and assistance for a time, but your future is largely in your own hands. You know that you have my very best wishes. You will keep in touch with us?"

"Yes."

"Good. And if you feel that I can help you in any way, do not hesitate to do as you have always done."

"Thank you, Doctor Timms."

"Good-bye, and good luck."

Mr Muir came alone to my bedside. As he stood, hands in pockets, smiling down at me, I remembered with amusement that I had once been frightened of this big man who was a tower of common sense, intellectual astuteness, and humour which was the basis of his quick understanding: an understanding that invariably startled his patients and his students because it seemed quite a simple matter for him to know what was going on in the other person's mind even while his own was solving orthopaedic problems or delivering lectures.

"You are sad, June?"

"Yes, Mr Muir. I am paying the penalty of being hopelessly spoilt."

His eyes lit for an instant. "I am glad to hear that, because you will understand when I tell you that you must not expect to be spoilt to this extent anywhere else. Because of the initial seriousness of your illness, and because you have been with us so long, it was inevitable that you should be spoilt . . . but——"

"I know, Mr Muir. Wherever I go, now, I shall be just another polio."

"Yes. And another thing for which you must prepare

yourself is the reaction of your friends in New Zealand. They did not see you in the lung, and they cannot be expected to believe how remarkable your recovery has been. Their pleasure at seeing you will be tinged with apprehension, and there will be some who will not be happy when they do see you."

"Can I do anything about it?"

"Yes, you can set about rehabilitating them, but you will find it more difficult than your own rehabilitation. Do you understand me?"

"Yes, yes. I think I do. They know me only as a strong, active person who could run, and swim, and dance, and so on, and they'll be more than a bit shattered to see me staggering about on crutches after all this time in hospital. I hadn't thought of that. I'll do my best, but I am not as old or as wise as St Mary's, you know."

He smiled then. "No—but you have a most commendable stubbornness. You will let us know of your progress?"

"Yes, Mr Muir."

"Hold fast to the ideas you have. Your recovery is not a question of luck or chance. My very best wishes go with you. Good-bye."

Exit the big man: enter Dr Casado.

"At last," he said, "I've got an innings. Every time I've looked in today someone has been leaning over your bed holding your hand. Tired?"

"No, Perez—but I've been thinking. I have become a child of two worlds. Two separate lives belonging to two countries on opposite sides of the globe. I love my mother and am longing to see her again, and I love New Zealand. They are my first life and my first love. But there is Mary's, and Mary's has given me a second life, so there is part of me that belongs here——"

"But you will be back?"

"Yes, I'll be back, sometime, somehow. I'll bring my mother and a large slice of New Zealand with me."

"Has your stay here been very irksome?"

"What a question! Of course it hasn't. You ought to know that. There are only two things that have driven me almost to screaming point, and they are both things that couldn't have been avoided, Mary's or no Mary's. They are trivial really, but it's trivial things that make us want to scream most times. The worst was the number of people that had to touch my body and the amount of handling it had to have; the other, the perpetual please and thank you brought about by my complete dependence on others. I knew it had to be, and that it was for my own good, and I'm not ungrateful, but I did get tired of being handled, and sometimes I forgot my pleases and thank yous, or muddled them up, or got so sick of the sound of them I went without things rather than have to utter them. Silly—but that is all over now, thank you very much, thank you very much, thank you——"

His hand closed over my mouth. "Silence! Even if you weren't able to call your body your own, you must admit you had control of your tongue, and that drove us to screaming point, especially when you sang. I shall never forget my first meeting with you . . . I thought you were finished, you know."

"Finished?"

"Yes, finished—done for. I even wrote you off as such in my diary." He grinned. "Don't sit there with your mouth open, I can see your tongue."

We talked for a long time and as he got up to go I said: "About tomorrow, Perez. No high-jinks, please."

He looked disappointed. "What—no red carpet, no band? We had quite a little banging ceremony ready. Can't I come and see you off?"

"Yes, I'd love you to, but Sister is coming to the boat with me, and I think we'd better exercise a little dignity."

Sister came as she was going off duty. She sat down on a chair by my bed and chuckled. "I don't know how I'm going to face the next patient in this bed."

"I never thought—of course, it will be free from tomorrow for Doctor Nairn. Someone booked already?"

"Yes, a heart. She'll be admitted, I expect, while I'm down at the boat with you."

I laughed. "That is typical of Mary's. No hesitation, no delay. Mend a body, and get another broken one in straight away."

"Now, have you got everything you need?"

"Yes, Sister, we've checked and rechecked. All the things I brought over, plus a lot more—even a champagne cork."

She smiled. "You are the most shocking accumulator."

"I know, but every time I look at that champagne cork I'll think of you. You're a bit like champagne, you know. Full of bubbles——" Then as I saw her face: "Not air bubbles, Sister. I meant full of sparkle."

But her head was back and she was laughing: then she sobered. "June, I shall miss you, but I have no fears as to your future. None at all. No matter what happens. You are a lucky girl because you have found the source of a really true and deep happiness very early in your life."

"For which I have to thank my illness, and Mary's, and you."

She flapped her hand at me. "What rubbish!" It was an evening to remember because Sister and I enjoyed the longest talk we had ever managed to have, alone.

Peter came at eight. I was in a rather madly hilarious mood, to which he matched his. But time came when he straightened his wide, smiling mouth, although his eyes still held laughter.

"Swan," he said, "have you ever thought about marriage?"

"Of course I have. Most normal young women in their twenties think about marriage, and I'm quite normal, you know. Or is that only my conceit?"

He grinned. "Conceit. You couldn't be normal no matter what happened to you, or how hard you tried."

"In that case it isn't much use you questioning me on a perfectly normal subject such as marriage, is it?"

"Oh, yes, I'd be interested to hear your views. In fact, I want to hear them. What are they?"

"Marriage is an alliance between members of the opposite sex to which no impediment should be admitted. It is solemnized in a church, made valid by law, and it is necessary for the propagation of——"

"Oh, shut up, Swan. I mean—as you know very well—in relation to yourself."

I put the tips of my fingers and thumbs together and gazed

262

into space. "Well, providing there is a chap about with a good skin and his own teeth—I don't mind gumminess, but I couldn't bear to trip over tumblers with sets of false teeth in them first thing in the morning. I shouldn't mind if he was bald, that's where the good skin comes in. I shouldn't mind if —Peter! mind what you're doing."

He had his hands round my throat. "I'll throttle you, my girl, if you won't be serious." He nodded his head slightly. "I know, I started it, but I retract with apologies. I'll even concede that you are normal, and I want an answer." He released his hands and he wasn't smiling any more.

"Marriage and me, Peter? Seriously?"

"Yes, please."

"All right. As I see it, it's a job requiring certain qualifications. I haven't got those qualifications yet, so I am not—um—eligible, shall we say?"

"But are you the one to consider whether you are eligible or not?"

"In my case, yes. I could not, and would not take it on as I am at present because I should fall down on it—literally. Question answered?"

"No, you could always be picked up and set to rights."

"But I couldn't accept the responsibility. And how could I get about a home?"

"You could have rails built along the walls."

"Now, look, Peter—I'll give you an instance. I want to scramble an egg for my husband's lunch. I have everything within my reach—no trouble, you say? But supposing this particular husband likes parsley in his scrambled egg and the parsley happens to be at the bottom of the garden. There's a rail out into the garden, so I go out, and what happens? I fall flat on my face stooping down to pick the parsley, and instead of a man coming home to scrambled egg, he comes home to find his wife at the bottom of the garden with a broken arm. Now, could you blame the poor fellow if he looked down at me and thought, 'What price holy matrimony?' Could you? and could you blame me for wondering if he was wondering if I was too much of a liability?"

"Strikes me, Swan, that most women are liabilities." He was smiling again. "One thing, you couldn't run out on a chap."

"I thought, Peter Johns, that it was your wish that we consider this matter seriously."

"Yes, but I can see that you've got a store of water-tight arguments to fling at me, and I do not propose to spend the next half-hour as we did on St Pancras Station. Remember all that waste of time and words? Now . . . you will get a lot more mobile, won't you?"

"Yes."

"And you will be back?"

"Yes."

"Quite definite on that point?"

"Quite definite."

Next morning the House Governor, the Matron, the physiotherapy staff, some of the students, and odd members of the hospital kept popping in. I thought I should never be dressed in time, but eventually we were all tidily stowed in the ambulance outside the hospital. Sister looking younger and merrier than usual in cinnamon brown which matched her eyes, and the nurse who was to accompany me beside her. I sat comfortably in my wheel-chair.

"Sister," I said, "you look very spicy. I should like to hang some red peppers on you."

There was a chuckle from the open doorway at the back of the ambulance, brown eyes flashed, and lips parted in a smile that everyone loved to see. "You'll have the sun, and the moon, and the stars to play with in the next few weeks, my Antipodean friend. Enjoy your trip."

"Thanks, Perez. I shall."

The door slammed shut and we pulled away from St Mary's. Our talk was not idle and most cheerful. Soon we were at the wharf, and I saw the boat that was to carry me across the sea, to my mother, and my homeland. No time for anything except a quick hug for Sister before four members of the crew carried me up the gangway. I held my arm high, and waved, hoping Sister would see: my back was towards her. I was, I thought,

264

turning my back on a lot of things and there was much ahead of me.

A new world: Captain, ship's doctor, purser, steward, and stewardess, and a nice little cabin with two beds. It looked incredibly small.

Nurse handed me a florist's box. Inside were some fragrant sprigs of lily-of-the-valley and a sealed envelope. A card in the latter, and on the card: "You could always grow your parsley in boxes outside the kitchen window. So now what?"